Fast Track to CAE

Longman

Fiona Joseph Peter Travis
with **Alan Stanton Susan Morris**

Exam Practice
Workbook

Pearson Education Limited
Edinburgh Gate
Harlow
Essex CM20 2JE
England
and associated companies throughout the world.
www.longman.com

First published 1999
Fifth impression 2001
ISBN 0 582 32359 2
Set in Slimbach and Univers
Printed in Spain by Gráficas Estella

Acknowledgements
We are grateful to the following for permission to reproduce copyright material:
Ewan MacNaughton Associates for an extract from the article 'Party warms to Towering Inferno charade' by Michael Fleet in *THE DAILY TELEGRAPH* 28.12.94; Gruner and Jahr Ltd for extracts from the articles 'Living in a TV time warp' by Green and Bodle in *FOCUS*, December 1995, 'Why should the sea level rise if global warming causes the icecaps to melt?' in *FOCUS* November 1995 and 'What's your poison?' by Trevor Day in *FOCUS* March 1996; Guardian Newspapers Ltd for extracts from the articles 'A dangerous way of life' in *GUARDIAN EDUCATION* 11.5.93, 'Stolen Innocence' in *THE GUARDIAN* 25.1.94, High Risk Factors' by Ed Douglas in *THE GUARDIAN* 17.2.94, 'The pressure point' by Angela Patmore in *THE GUARDIAN* 14.1.97 and 'How to write a blockbuster' in *THE GUARDIAN* 27.3.99; Independent Newspapers Ltd for extracts from the articles 'Goodbye to suburbia' by Andrew Adamson in *THE INDEPENDENT* 19.11.92, 'Me, just as I liked to be' by Jenni Murray in *THE INDEPENDENT* 5.5.93, 'All a Question of Keeping Faith' by Annette Morreau in *THE INDEPENDENT* 5.6.93 and 'Crossing the class barrier to create a happy family' by Kate Hilpern in *THE INDEPENDENT* 20.11.97; the author, Mary Killen, for an extract from her article 'No time like the last minute' in *SUNDAY TELEGRAPH* 29.9.96; Land's End Direct Merchants for an extract from 'A magical medium' by Tim Green in *LAND'S END CATALOGUE SPRING/SUMMER* 1995; National Magazine Co for extracts from the articles 'What are you going to be when you grow up?' by Purves, Boyt, Curling, Lampard and Darroch in *GOOD HOUSEKEEPING* June 1995 and ' In my heart, this is where I want to be' by Maggie Parham in *GOOD HOUSEKEEPING* August 1995 © National Magazine Company; Solo Syndication for extracts from the articles 'The don, the doctor and the noisy parkers' by Alun Rees in the *DAILY MAIL* 25.7.96, 'Are we living in a walk-on-by society?' in the *DAILY MAIL* 19.2.99 and 'James' story' in *YOU* Magazine; the writer, Rob Stepney, for an extract from his article 'Feeling Tired' in *THE INDEPENDENT* 15.5.93

Author acknowledgements
We would like to thank Dave Francis, our editor, for his invaluable editorial assistance at all stages of the project. We are also grateful to the students from Henley College, Coventry, Wulfrun College and the University of Wolverhampton who contributed their work to the Writing sections of the book. Fiona Joseph also acknowledges the support she received from the University of Wolverhampton Staff Development Committee.

Photo acknowledgements
We are grateful to the following for permission to reproduce copyright photographs: Pictor International for page: 17; Kobal Picture Collection for page: 29; Rex Features for page: 41; Redfurns Music Picture Library for page: 37; Telegraph Colour Library for page: 44; CFCL for page: 52; Tony Stone Images for page: 66; Jim Varney Photographer for page: 72; Hulton Getty for page: 77; Oxford Scientific Films for page: 81; Tony Stone Images for page: 91; Oxford Scientific Films for page: 95; Tony Stone Images for page: 105

Picture research by Image Select International Limited

Illustrated by Mik Brown

Produced for the publishers by David Francis

Dedication
For Anna

Contents

UNIT 1

Making an impression

READING
Part 1, Multiple matching

1 You are going to read an article from a newspaper in which a woman comments on a childhood photograph and the memories it evokes. Match each statement (1–12) with the person (A–E) in the text to whom it refers.

<table>
<tr><td colspan="2">Strategy</td></tr>
<tr><td>1</td><td>Read the instructions carefully to find out what you have to do.</td></tr>
<tr><td>2</td><td>Skim the text to get an idea of how it's organised and what it's about.</td></tr>
<tr><td>3</td><td>Scan the text and highlight references to the people listed.</td></tr>
<tr><td>4</td><td>Highlight key words in the questions and look for different ways of expressing these ideas.</td></tr>
</table>

Which person or persons

was angry about a lie that had been told?	**1**	**A** The writer
enjoyed their schooldays?	**2**	
liked adventure?	**3** **4**	**B** The mother
sent a relative to a school they had attended?	**5**	
failed to recognise a family member?	**6**	**C** The father
was rescued from a dangerous situation?	**7**	
decided to consult a parent?	**8**	**D** The head teacher
wanted the size of the family to increase?	**9**	
was summoned to see someone in authority?	**10**	**E** The friend, John Lewis
changed appearance in a way that upset people?	**11**	
became aware of judgements being made by others?	**12**	

2 Underline words or word combinations in the text which mean the same as:

1 a group of people living in the same area who have a strong bond between them (*para 2*)
2 loved very much (*para 2*)
3 an occasion when parents visit their child's school (*para 4*)
4 a distressing or unpleasant experience (*para 4*)
5 very annoyed or angry (*para 4*)
6 wanted something very much (*para 4*)
7 walked into water (*para 5*)
8 drastic (*para 6*)

3 Read the following sentences and underline the best option. All of these word combinations (which use adjective and adverb intensifiers) appear in the text you have just read.

1 I was *seriously/deeply/considerably* upset to hear about the death of the president.
2 After the operation to remove her appendix she was in an extremely *upset/serious/difficult* condition, but now she's absolutely *well/good/fine*.
3 Even for people who eat meat, the treatment of animals is not totally *agreeable/acceptable/right*.
4 I sometimes daydream about becoming rich but I know deep down that it's a/an *complete/real/actual* fantasy.
5 The police warned him that if he stole again, he would be in *terrifying/horrible/terrible* trouble.

Me, just as I liked to be

'WHEN I look at this photograph on my desk, I think to myself: 'That was the last time I could look at myself and feel totally happy with my image.' I'm about seven in the photo, and I look like the ultimate sweet little girl. But I know exactly what was going on in my head. That little girl is looking at the camera and thinking: 'I hate this. Why am I sitting here? When can I get into my cowboy outfit and go and play in the street?'

It was a school photograph taken in Barnsley, a town in the North of England, which was a very close-knit community. My mother had gone to the same school before me and I loved going there. Later I went to Barnsley Girls' High School, which my mother had also gone to, and I adored going there too.

I had no brothers or sisters. I'm an only child. I'm never quite sure if that is a good thing. In fact, it was about the time of this photograph that I told the biggest lie of my life about having a brother – and I got into the most terrible trouble.

My mother used to go to parents' evenings at the school, and after one of these I went in the next day and announced to the teachers that my mother was in hospital.

They said, 'Oh, why?' and I said, 'She's had a baby.' They said, 'Really? She seemed absolutely fine last night.' And I said, 'Oh yes, she was called in very late, and now I've got a little brother called David Robert.' It was the most awful trauma. The head teacher called my mother in and she was furious with me. It was a complete fantasy, but I longed to have a little brother, I absolutely longed for one, and I never got one.

I had a best friend called John Lewis who I used to play cowboys with. I remember there was a huge duckpond where we used to play, and trees we used to climb on. It was wonderful. John was trying to pick one of the flowers on the pond one day and fell into quite deep mud. I waded in but couldn't get him out and I remember being terribly frightened and realising that this was extremely serious, that the pond where we'd been playing all this time was actually quite deep and the mud was sucking us down. I managed to get out in the end and get a big stick which he grabbed hold of and I pulled him out.

Shortly after the photograph was taken, I went off on my own and had my hair cut very short, and my father was deeply upset about this, I was walking down the road when he was driving home from work. He didn't know who I was. He thought I was a boy. I would get on buses and people would call me 'son'. It was an incredibly radical change and everybody hated it. That was really the start of people saying, 'Your hair looks awful,' and then 'You're too thin' or 'You're too fat'. Somehow that was the point at which I started to grow up and people began to comment on my appearance as something other than totally acceptable.

I don't know any woman who is happy with the way she looks. But I can look at that photo and think, at that stage, I was happy with the way I was. Image is terribly important, and it's something about life that I hate.

VOCABULARY

Adjectives for describing people (CB pages 8/9)

1 Complete the following sentences with the correct form of the words in CAPITALS.

1 I must admit I find Chloe quite .... , but I don't think I'll get as far as asking her out! ATTRACT

2 I've never actually spoken to her. The problem is she doesn't look particularly .... APPROACH

3 Mary's the life and soul of the party – really .... GO

4 Graham's usually very quiet and shy, but he was quite .... when I met him yesterday. CHAT

5 Try not to wind Trevor up. I hate to say it but he can be quite .... at times. AGGRESSION

6 He likes to stay in each night and watch television. On balance he isn't what you'd call a very .... person. SOCIAL

7 Sandra's job involves her getting up at 5.30 a.m. each day. Is it any wonder she's so .... ? TEMPER

8 You should see the way my older brother dresses. I suppose on his salary he can afford to look so smart and .... GROOM

Tip: Remember that the main ways of making adjectives from nouns or verbs are 1) to add the endings *-ive, -able, -y, -ed* and/or 2) to put a prefix or another word in front of the noun or verb to modify the meaning. You will have another test of this in Unit 4.

Connotation (CB page 9)

2 In each of these sentences, there are two words which are similar in meaning but the second word has a more negative association (or connotation). <u>Underline</u> the word that is most appropriate in each sentence.

1 Jon won't stop playing on that new computer of his. He's becoming really *passionate/obsessive* about it.

2 Order now from our brand-new catalogue. We also specialise in clothes for the *larger/obese* woman.

3 Police are still looking for the *famous/notorious* serial killer who is now thought to be living in Germany.

4 I'm enjoying my new teaching job apart from the fact that the pupils are rather *friendly/familiar* with the staff.

5 Don't be so *innocent/naive*. Can't you see she's trying to twist you round her little finger?

6 So you're getting driving lessons for your next birthday? I wish my parents were as *generous/over-indulgent* as yours.

7 The proposal to pay staff at the company a bonus for working longer hours was a *shrewd/sly* one.

8 The thing I like about Daniel is his *trusting/gullible* nature.

Phrasal verbs (CB pages 11/12)

3 Look at the list of verbs (1–8) and match each one with a less formal phrasal verb (A–H) that is similar in meaning.

1	resign	A	put (somebody) forward (for/as something)
2	depress		
3	terminate	B	give in
4	nominate	C	choke back
5	suppress	D	get (somebody) down
6	confess	E	break off (something)
7	reprimand	F	own up
8	surrender	G	hand in (your notice)
		H	tell (somebody) off

4 Complete these dialogues with one of the phrasal verbs from Exercise 3 in the correct form.

1 A: Charlie can be quite dishonest, can't he?
   B: Yes, you'll never catch him .... to any of his tricks.

2 A: My boss at work is a real bully.
   B: In that case, make sure you don't .... to her. And whatever happens, don't be tempted to .... your notice.

3 A: Is there much competition in the elections that are coming soon?
   B: I'm expecting Cherry Knowles to .... herself .... as a candidate.

4 A: Do you remember that really sad song – now how does it go?
   B: You mean 'Rainy days and Mondays always .... me .... '.

5 A: That's the last time I go and see a Spielberg film.
   B: I thought I saw you trying to .... the tears in the cinema.

6 A: Tom and Tina don't seem very happy these days.
   B: Haven't you heard? She's .... their engagement.

7 A: Looking back, I must have been quite a naughty child.
   B: Why? Were your parents always .... you .... ?

ENGLISH IN USE
Part 1, Multiple choice cloze (CB page 15)

For questions **1–10**, read the text below and then decide which word (**A, B, C** or **D**) best fits each space. Put the letter you choose for each question (**A–D**) in the gap. There is a clue after each question to help you. The exercise begins with an example (**0**).

Strategy

Read the text all the way through to start with before you focus on each gap in turn. While you are reading, try to guess what the missing words are before you start to look at the options.

FEELING TIRED

A year ago, Laura reached her lowest (**0**) .A. . Utterly exhausted after a short walk, she was (**1**) .... up off the pavement and driven home by the police. 'My feet felt nailed to the ground,' she recalls. With permanent flu (**2**) .... , panic stricken and confined to a wheelchair, she was eventually diagnosed as having chronic fatigue syndrome, the term doctors now use for her illness. Laura, a 30-year-old marketing manager, has since made a remarkable (**3**) .... in her health. She is now able to walk for an hour, swims twenty lengths three times a week and is (**4**) .... going back to work. She (**5**) .... her new-found sense of well-being down to a technique called cognitive behaviour therapy. CBT aims to help people understand how the beliefs they (**6**) .... about themselves and others influence mood and behaviour – and how re-evaluating negative beliefs can help them to feel and behave differently. It has been successful in dealing with problems ranging from depression to chronic, unexplained pain. Research shows that CBT can also help people like Laura. Yet many sufferers are (**7**) .... opposed to the treatment, arguing that their (**8**) .... is physical not psychological. Psychological therapy, they believe, implies that they are to (**9**) .... and their disorder is not genuine. Laura says CBT helped her change the way she thought about her problems without implying that they were her fault. 'I was an "all-or-nothing" thinker and felt I had to be perfect in everything. The therapy has encouraged a less perfectionist approach to life and helped me gradually to (**10**) .... up more physical activity.'

0	**A** point	**B** mark	**C** time	**D** degree

1	**A** collected	**B** moved	**C** taken	**D** picked

Clue: This is a phrasal verb with a literal meaning.

2	**A** indications	**B** signs	**C** symptoms	**D** characteristics

Clue: Which of these words do you associate most strongly with illness or medical matters?

3	**A** renewal	**B** return	**C** recovery	**D** restoration

Clue: Which word do you most associate with getting better after an illness?

4	**A** contemplating	**B** regarding	**C** reflecting	**D** judging

Clue: Only one of these words comes before an '-ing' form – 'going'.

5	**A** puts	**B** gets	**C** takes	**D** turns

Clue: Which phrasal verb has the form 'to .... sth down to sth' meaning 'to explain or account for sth'?

6	**A** carry	**B** hold	**C** keep	**D** possess

Clue: You need a verb which collocates strongly with the noun 'beliefs'.

7	**A** intensively	**B** extremely	**C** bitterly	**D** severely

Clue: Which adverb collocates the most strongly with 'opposed'?

8	**A** condition	**B** state	**C** case	**D** circumstance

Clue: You need a noun which collocates with the adjectives 'physical' and 'psychological'. If someone has an illness you may talk about their 'medical …'

9	**A** criticise	**B** blame	**C** accuse	**D** disapprove

Clue: Which fixed expression means that something is your fault?

10	**A** mount	**B** grow	**C** build	**D** develop

Clue: This is part of a phrasal verb meaning 'increase the amount of sth' (in this case 'physical activity').

LANGUAGE STUDY

Modal verbs review (CB pages 12/13)

1 Underline the correct form of the verb in the following sentences. Then categorize each group under the uses below. The first one has been done as an example. In one of the sentences both answers are correct.

(L) degrees of likelihood
(A) ability
(P) permission
(O) obligation
(N) necessity (or lack of necessity)

1 (L)
   a) Tony *must have been*/*must have* run into heavy traffic. He should have arrived by now.
   b) He *won't have*/*won't* be here in time for dinner.
   c) He *can't have*/*can have* called. I've been in all evening and haven't heard the phone.

2 ( )
   a) Apparently, you *mustn't*/*don't have to* enter the country without a visa.
   b) I know you *don't have to*/*mustn't* have a visa if you're travelling from Spain.
   c) I *have to*/*must* remember to get my passport renewed.

3 ( )
   a) Sue *doesn't need to*/*needn't have to*/*didn't need to* worry. I'm sure she'll pass the exam.
   b) I *needn't have*/*didn't need* worried about the interview. I got the job quite easily.

4 ( )
   a) You *can't to*/*are not allowed to* smoke until you're 16 in England.
   b) I *was allowed to*/*could* stay out until quite late as a child.

5 ( )
   a) The bank was closed so I *couldn't*/*wasn't able to* get any money out.
   b) I *could*/*was able to* get some from the cashpoint by the supermarket

2 The following sentences are too formal. Rewrite each sentence using the word in **brackets**.

1 We are obliged to tell the teacher if we're going to be late. (*have*)

....

2 You weren't compelled to help me but thanks all the same. (*need*)

....

3 You can dispense with the dictionary. The text is quite easy. (*need*)

....

4 Were you successful in booking a table at the restaurant? (*able*)

....

5 My parents have never permitted me to have a party. (*allowed*)

....

6 He will in all probability have decided to stay at home. (*must*)

....

7 I worried unnecessarily about the exam. It was easy. (*have*)

....

8 We are not authorised to proceed beyond this point. (*must*)

....

9 I won't be capable of meeting you at 9.00. (*able*)

....

10 I am sure that isn't John at the door. He's still at work. (*can*)

....

Past simple, present perfect simple and continuous (CB page 16)

3 Complete the second sentence so that it has the same meaning as the first.

1 This is my first time in Italy.
   I .... Italy before.

2 When did you first meet Peter?
   How long .... Peter?

3 This is my sixth month now without a cigarette.
   I .... for six months.

4 I'm still doing my homework.
   I .... yet.

5 This is my third bar of chocolate today.
   So far .... three bars of chocolate today.

6 Did he really only start learning to drive three weeks ago?
   Has .... to drive for three weeks?

7 The suspect was last seen running away from the bank.
   The suspect .... since he ran away from the bank.

8 The last time I hired a car was on holiday last year.
   I .... my last holiday.

4 Write the correct form of the verb in brackets. Change the word order if necessary. There may be more than one answer.

1 A: Bill! At last! I .... (try) to contact you all afternoon. Where .... (you/be)?

   B: Sorry, I .... (sit) in meetings all day and I only .... (get) back here a few minutes ago.

2 A: .... (you/speak) to Claire yet?

   B: No. I .... (try) to call her a few times but she .... (be) engaged each time.

3 A: I .... (have) this car almost four years now and it .... (never give) me any trouble.

   B: Really? I .... (have) a few problems with mine lately.

4 A: How long .... (you two/know) each other?

   B: Oooh, I don't know. .... (we not meet) at the sales conference?

5 A: Carlos, you look exhausted! What .... (you/do)?

   B: I .... (read) all about phrasal verbs. They're fascinating! I .... (already read) four chapters.

6 A: What .... (you/do) with my dictionary? I can't find it anywhere.

   B: I .... (use) it to write my essay. Can I give it back to you when I've finished?

7 A: What .... (you/do) with my dictionary? All the pages are dirty.

   B: Oh, sorry. I .... (drop) it on the way to college.

8 I .... (live) in the same town all my life. I can't ever imagine leaving.

9 They .... (live) in rented accommodation since their house was flooded.

ENGLISH IN USE
Part 3, Error correction

1 The error correction task consists of a short text in which many of the lines contain an extra word. The extra word is often one of the following categories.

- prepositions
- phrasal verbs
- auxiliary verbs
- comparatives (*more, less,* etc.)
- articles
- conjunctions
- relative pronouns
- personal pronouns
- quantifiers

In the following extracts from 'Role-playing with Attitude' from the Coursebook page 11, match the words in *italics* with each of the categories above.

1 He *winds* me *up*.

2 *Most* of the pupils admit they *have* volunteered *because* they are shy.

3 Assertiveness training is growing *in* pockets around *the* country.

4 Perhaps the *most* important lesson is to realise ....

5 *It* is an area *where* we have to tread very carefully.

2 Underline the extra word in each sentence below. Match each underlined word to a category in Exercise 1.

Example:

Having <u>had</u> to use a computer all the time can cause eyestrain. ...*auxiliary verb*...

1 The driver that he caused the accident was arrested for dangerous driving. ....

2 We arrived to home at about 11.00 o'clock. ....

3 We've decided to go travelling around the Europe. ....

4 Can you pay me back some that money you owe me? ....

5 Sam put me up with over the weekend. ....

6 Although the party was great, but the food was terrible. ....

7 If you were more fitter, you wouldn't suffer so much from aches and pains. ....

8 There's a heavy traffic congestion in the city centre this evening. ....

9 The teams were played for most of the first half without scoring. ....

10 I just couldn't seem to get over to the point I wanted to make. ....

WRITING

Part 2, Formal letter (CB pages 17–19)

1 Read this writing task.

You have seen the following job advertisement and have decided to apply for the job.

Wanted!

Enthusiastic and energetic social organisers for a children's summer school situated in the beautiful Welsh countryside. Candidates will need to be between the ages of 18 and 35, have experience in supervising various sporting activities and be able to motivate young teenagers. You will need to speak fluent English as well as at least one other foreign language. A driving licence is essential. Please send a letter of application outlining your suitability for the post to the following address: Summer Sensation, Langdon Farm, Cardiff.

Write your **letter of application**. (Write approximately 250 words.)

2 Read the mark scheme for the task. This will tell you what the examiner is looking for in an ideal answer.

Content (points covered): the letter must mention the applicant's age, relevant experience, ability to motivate, fluency in two languages, driving licence.
Organisation and cohesion: the letter should be divided into clear paragraphs, e.g.
  paragraph 1 – reason for writing
  paragraphs 2/3 – career history, evidence of experience and skills
  paragraph 4 – personal qualities, general suitability for the job
  paragraph 5 – concluding remarks.
Range: must use language suited to a letter of application i.e. appropriate tenses (*I have been working with children for …* ; *During my holidays I worked …*), set expressions (*I am writing with reference to …*).
Register: fairly formal.
Target reader: would be convinced that this person is a suitable candidate.
Accuracy: should not contain major errors that lead to misunderstandings or have a negative effect on the reader.

3 Now read the answer on page 11 and do the questions below.

1 Has the writer included all the essential information? Tick off the list in Exercise 2, **Content**. Is there any information that has been included unnecessarily? If so, cross it out. What extra information has he included that would make a good impression? Highlight it and put a tick (✓) next to it.
2 a) Has the writer organised the letter appropriately? Use the paragraph organisation in Exercise 2 to help you decide which paragraphs could be joined together.
  b) Does it begin and end appropriately?
  c) Are the linking expressions *however*, *moreover* and *in fact* used correctly?
3 a) Underline four set expressions that the writer uses that could be used in *any* letter of application and put a tick (✓) next to them.
  b) Underline and correct a mistake with tenses in the first paragraph.
4 Find these errors, make the necessary corrections:
  incorrect use of punctuation/capitals (*para 1*)
  incorrect use of an article (*paras 2 and 3*)
  spelling mistakes (*para 3*)
  an informal word (*para 6*)

4 Now rewrite the answer using the corrections that you have made.

Dear Sirs,

1   I wish to apply for the position of 'Social organiser for children' in the daily mirror. I started to look after children from 11 to 20 since I was 20. I have had until now 7 years experience.

2   As you can see in my CV, I have both a sound experience in organising young people and children who I have supervised were from several countries, so my fluency in English, Spanish and French was very useful.

3   I had to assume several responsibilities for a two-month countryside camp in Edinburgh. We also partcipated in a swimming gala. Few of the children were experienced at this. However, after two weeks of hard pratising and encouragement, they won the second place. Moreover, Garry Addams, the famous swimmer, was so imprest by the children's performance gave them a free membership.

4   My own abilities in rock-climbing, horse-riding and canoeing gave me the opportunity to supervise many outdoor sports and activities, where children enjoyed trying them; for example, shooting and archery.

5   One of my duties was to drive a mini-bus. In fact, I have been driving for 9 years. As an added requirement, I also have my Gold Lifesaving Certificate.

6   I really feel that my abilities meet your requirements. I hope you will give my application serious consideration.

7   I look forward to hearing from you.

Yours faithfully

Pablo Arrieta

MR PABLO ARRIETA

Going too far

READING

Part 4, Multiple matching

1 You are going to read an article from a magazine in which five people talk about significant events in their careers. Match each statement (**1–12**) with the person (**A–E**) in the text to whom it refers.

Tip: The examiner wants you to be able to read quickly and efficiently. Time yourself and try to do this test without using a dictionary.

Which person		
rejected one career because it involved travelling?	**1**	
felt he/she was being judged personally, and not by the work he/she had done?	**2**	**A** Jockey
learned more about a subject that had been studied previously?	**3**	
achieved a goal with a companion?	**4**	**B** Barrister
does not expect huge financial rewards?	**5**	
finds similarities with another job?	**6**	**C** Novelist
felt tired after physical exertion?	**7**	
is surprised at the prestige of a particular profession?	**8**	**D** Mountaineer
was interested in this activity at an early age?	**9**	
realises he/she did something unwise and dangerous?	**10**	**E** Sculptor
had to consider his/her family?	**11**	
takes no notice of possible criticisms of his/her work?	**12**	

2 What is the correct name for a person who does the following? Put each word in the appropriate box in the table. The first has been done as an example.

A person who ...

1 produces films.
2 types.
3 supervises others.
4 plays music professionally.
5 is employed by a company.
6 writes reports for newspapers.
7 gives instruction to others.
8 is being trained for their job.
9 gives therapy to people.
10 studies history.

-ist	-er	-or	-ee	-ian
	film producer			

What are you going to be when you grow up?

There's nothing more terrifying, or thrilling, than plunging into the career you always dreamed of. Five people look back on starting out.

A Jockey

Even though I'd been around horses an awful lot – ridden since I was three and worked in racehorse yards since fifteen – nothing can prepare you for your first race. Mine was at a race in Devon. My horse was what we call 'an old schoolmaster', a fifteen-year-old who basically taught me the ropes. I just pointed him at the jumps – there were eighteen of them – and off we went. It passed in a flash, was terribly exhilarating, and although I didn't fall off, I did have a bit of a close call at one jump. I came fourth in the race, didn't win a thing though. Anyway, the prize money is so low, you'll never get rich in this game.

B Barrister

I used to be an opera singer but switched to a barrister because to make progress as a singer I'd have had to be on tour, away from my family for long periods, and I also needed a more reliable source of income. My first case was defending a woman found with an offensive weapon. In terms of stage fright, I felt exactly the same as before an opera performance. I think I need that sort of adrenalin to get me firing on all cylinders. But there are big differences too. In an opera, the lines are scripted for you. In court, it comes as a shock to have to make up your own dialogue and all sorts of unexpected things can happen. Another thing is that when you're singing, you put all your emotion into it. Now it's my intellectual capacity that is needed, and I'm always being told that I show my feelings too much. I'll get the balance right soon, I hope. When I win cases, I get a different kind of triumph from a good performance on stage. It gives me a real sense of achievement that beats all the applause. What amazed me most was how much higher a barrister is esteemed than a singer. People were impressed about my going into court in a way they weren't about my going on stage.

C Novelist

I always wanted to write a novel but it was something I never had the nerve to do. When, as an English literature student at university, I read even the lighter classics I was so impressed by their sheer craftsmanship that it seemed impertinent to try and do something similar. So, although I wrote a few stories for magazines, the novel remained unattempted. But the idea was still in my mind, as the ultimate desirable thing to do. To be an absolute beginner at the age of forty-five is probably good for the soul. There you are, aware of what you can do and adept at avoiding what you can't. And then you plunge recklessly into someone else's craft with no idea at all whether you can do it. For a newspaper journalist, the shock is having so much space. Then there is also the problem of not knowing which kind of novelist you are. Even if only three people buy my book, even if the reviewers call it rubbish and the booksellers hide it under piles of autobiographies, it will have served a purpose. I know a great deal more now about how novels work than I ever did while I was studying them non-stop for three years. It is a good feeling.

D Mountaineer

My first major climb was Mont Blanc – until then it had all been hill-walking – and I went with my sister. The beginning is warm and friendly. You set off in a little mountain train and then walk up a safe, rocky path. Then we spent the night in a little Alpine hut, but hardly slept because we were so excited. Breakfast is usually served at 2 a.m. because it gets too hot to climb later in the day. We left at 1 a.m. to avoid the other climbers and climbed all the way up in the dark, although there was a wonderful moon and we could see a line of torches behind us. We reached the summit at dawn. We went back down a different way, over a glacier, which, with hindsight, we shouldn't have done because neither of us knew anything about crevasse rescue, and it is very easy to fall in. But we didn't think about it twice and got down safely. The last bit was such a relief, because there's a cable car and you can put your feet up.

E Sculptor

My first public commission was a half-size bronze horse, a model of 'Golden Miller', a winner at Cheltenham race-course. Just before the unveiling of the statue, I realised the significance of what I'd done – there were TV cameras, art critics, the public ... I felt as if I was being unveiled. Two jockeys who had ridden the horse were there, and one of them said, 'If I don't like it, I'll say so.' There was a hush when the veil came off, followed by spontaneous clapping. Then the jockey said, 'It's the horse itself.' I felt so relieved, as if I'd got my clothes back on again.

---

3 Complete the following sentences with the correct prepositions from the box.

with into to at for (×2) by in

1 George was lucky to survive the accident when his car smashed .... the tree.
2 We were deeply saddened .... the news of your cousin's death.
3 Wendy likes adventure but she lives a bit too close .... the edge at times.
4 Your sister doesn't care about who she's cheeky to – she's got no respect .... authority.
5 Paul is getting bored with his job. He might throw it all .... for a bit of excitement.
6 Simon has become obsessed .... that new computer game.
7 It's very easy for people to shake their heads .... those who do dangerous sports.
8 Theresa has got a bit of a reputation .... getting into trouble with the police.

VOCABULARY

Adjectives for describing feelings
(-ed and -ing endings) (CB pages 20/21)

Tip: Adjectives for describing feelings (or what something is like) are useful for the second part of the Speaking Paper, where you should try to give a personal response to the picture prompts. The examiners will be more impressed if you choose the correct adjective ending!

1 Group the following adjectives (1–10) in the chart below according to their meaning. Most of these words also have an -ing form. Find the two words which don't and supply the correct form.

1 delighted	6 terrified
2 tested	7 stimulated
3 enthralled	8 motivated
4 thrilled	9 scared
5 engrossed	10 taxed

exhilarated	petrified	challenged	absorbed	inspired

2 Underline the correct word in each sentence. The sentences refer to the pictures on page 20 of the Coursebook.

1 I'd be *terrified/terrifying* in a similar situation.
2 It must have been *enthralled/enthralling* to watch.
3 My life is nowhere near as *stimulated/stimulating*.
4 I'm afraid I'm not *inspired/inspiring* by these photographs to try anything similar.
5 I'd find a situation like this quite *delighted/delightful*.
6 I'm *intrigued/intriguing* as to why people do such things.
7 It must be *thrilling/thrilled* to do something like this.
8 I'd like to do something *challenged/challenging* like that.

3 Look at the following statements and choose an adjective from Exercise 1 with the right meaning *and* the right form to replace the colloquial expressions in *italics*.

1 That detective story was great – it was .... (*impossible to put down*).
2 What a wonderful painting. I'm really .... (*fired up*) now to have a go myself.
3 That computer training course was .... (*a bit tricky*) but I enjoyed it.
4 I was .... (*over the moon*) when they told me I'd passed the exam.
5 There's something about him I don't like. He is .... (*gives me the creeps*).

Collocation

4 Underline the correct verb in each sentence below.

1 Eating a high-fat diet is likely to *lay/leave/put* people at risk of heart disease.
2 This is the last time I'm going to *hold/stick/push* my neck out for you. Next time you'll have to get the job done yourself.
3 A: Do you think I can get away with leaving work early again today?
   B: Just don't *drive/press/push* your luck.
4 I wouldn't get too friendly with your boss. You could be *playing/working/going* with fire!
5 Car fumes and other forms of pollution *raise/pose/risk* a serious threat to public health.
6 I'm fed up with city life. I've finally decided to *take/make/do* the plunge and move to the country.
7 A: Are you going to wear your raincoat?
   B: Yes, it would be *tempting/attracting/charming* fate not to, wouldn't it?
8 He'll be *begging/sending/asking* for trouble if he doesn't get his car serviced soon.

5 Put each of the sentences (1–8) above in one of the following categories. Write the correct numbers on the lines.

1 Doing something that seems stupid because it involves unnecessary risks. (These expressions can be used to warn somebody not to do something foolish.)
....
....
2 Causing risks for someone or society in general.
....
3 Deciding to do something even though it may be risky.
....

Phrasal verbs (CB page 26)

6 Some metaphorical phrasal verbs can be understood by looking at the literal meaning of the verb. Using a good dictionary to help you if necessary, match each of the verbs with their literal meanings. The first one has been done as an example.

Main verb		Literal meaning
1	iron	A fasten or bind with rope, string, etc.
2	pour	B wander for pleasure with no special destination in mind
3	tie	C go round something in a circle, e.g. the earth round the sun
4	revolve	D cut e.g. food (usually meat), or wood
5	rake	E be on the edge of something, e.g. a piece of land
6	polish	F rub something e.g. piece of furniture to make it shiny
7	ramble	G remove wrinkles and creases from clothes
8	border	H gather dead leaves together
		I cause liquid, e.g. water, to flow in a continuous stream
9	carve	

7 The following sentences contain a phrasal verb which has been used more metaphorically. Complete each sentence using one of the verbs above in its correct grammatical form. (The particles are already given.)

Example: The new computer system that we've installed should ....*iron*....... *out* most of our payment problems.

1 My great uncle is always .... *on* about the good old days. It's so boring for everyone else to listen to!

2 Once Sara had gained her trust, Dot began to .... *out* all her emotions.

3 Adam's French is getting really rusty. He'll have to .... it *up* a little before his next meeting in Paris.

4 Tara and Ben are such a carefree couple – you can tell that they're not going to be .... *down* by marriage and children.

5 It might be a relatively small company at the moment but it's aiming to .... *out* a good slice of the telecommunications market before long.

6 It must be difficult being a doctor, where your life .... *around* the job.

7 I wish you would stop talking about how happy you were in France. It's no good .... *over* the past.

8 That joke just isn't funny. In fact, it's .... *on* being offensive.

ENGLISH IN USE

Part 4, Word formation (CB page 30)

1 Read the following text and decide whether the missing word in each case is likely to be a verb, a general noun or personal noun, an adjective or an adverb. When you have decided, choose the correct form of the base word below and complete the gaps.

Tip: To do this question successfully you have to be able to 1) identify the part of speech that is needed in the gap and 2) form the word correctly (e.g. by adding an affix, making internal changes, or forming a compound word).

ON TOP OF THE WORLD

To many people **(1)** .... seems a very uncomfortable and **(2)** .... sport, full of hardships and dangers. To **(3)** .... , however, the dangers are accepted in return for the thrill of conquering high peaks. Of course, from time to time, we read of **(4)** .... accidents especially when climbers are operating at the limits of human **(5)** .... But if you have the right equipment, a head for **(6)** .... , good training and you climb within your capabilities, there is no reason why this sport should not be as safe as many other **(7)** .... Climbers themselves would argue that nothing else brings the same degree of truly **(8)** .... exhilaration and excitement.

(1)	MOUNTAIN	**(5)**	ENDURE
(2)	RISK	**(6)**	HIGH
(3)	ENTHUSE	**(7)**	ACTIVE
(4)	TRAGEDY	**(8)**	BELIEVE

Reminder: When you record a new word in your vocabulary notebook, note down its related forms and their part of speech as well.

LANGUAGE STUDY

Review of relative clauses (CB page 25)

1 Make the following sentences more formal by placing the preposition before a relative pronoun. You may need to change the form of the relative pronoun.

Example:
That's a subject they often disagreed about.
That's a subject about which they often disagreed. (F)

1 He met Susan, who he got married to, in 1967.
2 She's a teacher who the students have a lot of respect for.
3 We flew to Amsterdam, where we caught our connecting flight from.
4 South Africa is the country which we get most of our gold from.
5 That's the officer who I was speaking to.
6 That's the point which I was referring to.

2 Rewrite this letter to include the extra information below in the places indicated, using relative clauses.

Dear Sir or Madam

I am writing about the article 'The high-flyer' (1).

The journalist concerned (2) fails to understand the most basic point. Professional stunt men do not take risks unnecessarily. They work under strictly controlled conditions (3). This is completely different from Darren Newton's stunt (4).

This was carried out at the Hilton Hotel, a very public place (5). The journalist does not seem to realise such stunts endanger members of the public (6). How would he feel if he were innocently walking down the road when someone tried out a similar stunt? (7)

I feel very strongly that newspapers like yours (8) should show a more responsible attitude.

Yours faithfully

1 It appeared in your newspaper recently.
2 He seemed supportive of these dangerous stunts.
3 Safety is of paramount importance in these environments.
4 The stunt was described in the article.

5 Little was done at the Hilton to warn people of the stunt.
6 People may well be unaware of what is happening.
7 The stunt caused personal injury to him.
8 Newspapers like yours have an enormous influence.

Tip: You may be tested on punctuation in the error correction question in the English in Use Paper. Remember that defining relative clauses do not have a comma, and that non-defining ones do. (See Exercise 3 on relative clauses in the Coursebook page 25.)

Review of narrative tenses (CB page 27)

3 <u>Underline</u> the correct tense in the following sentences.

1 I *had got up/got up* this morning an hour earlier than I *needed/had needed* to.
2 We *had been/were* working for two hours when we finally *had decided/decided* to have a rest.
3 I *was crossing/crossed* the road this morning when a car *was coming/came* round the corner and nearly *was hitting/hit* me.
4 When he *had opened/opened* the door he *was seeing/saw* a letter lying on the floor.
5 When they *had finished/finished* discussing the project they *went/were going* to the restaurant.
6 It was early morning; people *were rushing/rushed* to catch their trains and the shopkeepers *were getting/got* ready to open up.

4 Complete this report about a real mountain rescue. Use the correct tense of the verbs in brackets.

Mountain Rescue
Nine hikers (1) .... (reach) the top of Griffith Peak one Sunday afternoon and (2) .... (prepare) to start their descent. On the way down they (3) .... (split up) into three separate groups. One female hiker (4) .... (decide) to hike back to the middle group to help her friend who (5) .... (suffer) with an injured knee. On the way back she (6) .... (go) off the trail and the group she (7) .... (look) for (8) .... (walk) past her without noticing her. She (9) .... (able) to get back on the trail and (10) .... (continue) to walk until the summit. She (11) .... (decide) to stay there, thinking that her friends would be back for her. However, all three groups (12) .... (arrive) in separate vehicles, so when each group (13) .... (return) to their cars

they (14) .... (leave) thinking she was with the other group. She (15) .... (have) to spend the night up the mountain. Her boyfriend (16) .... (think) she (17) .... (go) home to her parents and her parents (18) .... (presume) she (19) .... (stay) with her boyfriend, so nobody (20) .... (know) she (21) .... (miss) until Monday afternoon. By this time the woman (22) .... (decide) to make her way down but again (23) .... (get) lost. Five teams (24) .... (go) by ground and air to various parts of the trail. One of the teams eventually (25) .... (find) her and (26) .... (fly) her in a helicopter to base camp.

ENGLISH IN USE

Part 3, Error correction (CB page 31)

1 Some but not all of the lines in the following text contain one extra word that should not be there. Read the text through to find out what it's about then <u>underline</u> the unnecessary words and tick (✓) the lines that are correct. The exercise begins with two examples (**0**).

2 How many times did the following grammatical errors appear in the text? Write down the line numbers next to each category.

incorrect use of an article ....
incorrect tense structure ....
incorrect use of a preposition ....
mistakes in relative clauses ....
unnecessary use of time linking words ....

3 If you got lines 1, 12 and 15 wrong, read page 198 of the Coursebook again. If you got lines 5 and 8 wrong, read page 199.

THE HISTORY OF BUNGEE JUMPING

0 ✓ Bungee jumping is a relatively recent sport and one which has become

0 very popular. However, few <u>of</u> people know of the origins of this risky sport.

1 Bungee jumping was being inspired by the vine jumpers of Pentecost Island

2 in the Pacific Ocean Vanuatu group (formerly the New Hebrides). Each

3 year, the men of the island's tribe construct up the huge wooden towers,

4 hundreds of feet high. They then carefully select vines from the jungle

5 which they then tie them to their ankles before throwing themselves off

6 the top of the towers. The length and age of the vines must be so carefully

7 judged so that the vine stops their fall just as they hit on the ground. Inspired

8 by the islanders, whose modern bungee jumping was invented by members of

9 The Oxford University Dangerous Sports Club. Using a special nylon

10 cord instead of vines, and dressed in their customary top hat and tails, when

11 they performed a four person simultaneous jump from the Clifton Suspension

12 Bridge in Bristol on April 1st 1979. The D.S.C. has been performed many

13 other jumps, including one off the Golden Gate Bridge. During the 1980s

14 A.J. Hackett opened the first commercial jump site in New Zealand.

15 As part of the site publicity, Hackett had performed an astounding bungee

16 jump from the Eiffel Tower right in the centre of Paris.

WRITING

Part 1, Formal letter (CB pages 28/29)

1 Read this writing task.

You recently bought the CRAZEE 4 YOU package described in the advert below for your nine-year-old niece. However, when she came to play the video she realised that she had already seen it. You were refused a refund when you took it back to the shop, in spite of the fact that the package came with a money-back guarantee. You have decided to put your complaint in writing. Using the information in the advert and the notes that you have made, as well as the letter to your sister, write a letter to the store manager explaining why you are not satisfied and suggesting appropriate compensation.

Dear Sis

Just wanted to write and say how sorry I am that Emily was disappointed with her birthday present. If I'd known she'd already seen the video I'd never have bought it. Would you believe the shop wouldn't give me my money back for the video because it had already been watched! As soon as the fan-club membership arrives I'll pass it on to her, although I've been waiting two weeks already . . .

some of them are really fuzzy black and white pictures

SPECIAL OFFER

Top of the charts group **CRAZEE 4 YOU** are proud to bring you this special offer. For just £30.00 and for a limited period only you can buy a complete package of video, book and tee shirt with the **CRAZEE 4 YOU** logo.

The video includes over 30 minutes of <u>exclusive</u> footage, and the book contains over 200 <u>top-quality photographs</u>.

If you buy within 30 days you will also receive <u>instant free membership</u> to our fan club.

The offer comes with our <u>money-back guarantee</u>.

Not true — this was on TV last week!

still waiting ...

shop assistant refused to give money back for the video

2 Read the mark scheme for the task. This will tell you what the examiner is looking for in an ideal answer.

Content (points covered): the letter must mention the following reasons for complaint:
– video is not in fact exclusive
– poor quality of the photographs
– membership has not arrived
– your niece's disappointment
– you weren't able to get a refund despite the promise of a money-back guarantee and a suggestion of compensation.

Organisation and cohesion: the letter should be well organised and the events told in a logical way, e.g.
    paragraph 1 – reason for writing
    paragraph 2 – reason for buying the product

paragraph 3 – why you were unhappy with it
paragraph 4 – what action you would like the shop to take.

Range: the letter should use common expressions for writing about a complaint and asking for compensation. (See Language Bank on CB page 29)

Register: fairly formal.

Target reader: the store manager would have a clear understanding of the problem and be sympathetic to it, enough to wish to offer compensation.

Accuracy: should not contain major errors that lead to misunderstandings or have a negative effect on the reader.

3 Now read this answer and do the questions below.

Dear Sir

1   I'm writing this letter because I'm sure you can help me to
   overcome an unpleasant situation caused by my purchase of your
   'Crazee 4 You' package.

   When I read the description of your special offer in the
5   advertisement, I immediately thought about my niece: she is
   literally 'crazee for them', one of their greatest fans without any
   doubts!

   Since I was looking for two birthday presents for her, I decided
   that your package was the perfect gift for my nine-year-old Emily
10   and I bought it.

   I was sure I had made the right choice, at least until the day she
   phoned me to tell me that she has already seen the video —
   described as 'exclusive' in the advert — on TV the week before,
   that some of the 'top-quality photographs' were just blurred black
15   and white pictures and that the free membership to your fan club
   wasn't included (she's still waiting for it now, after two weeks!).

   Although the package had come with a money-back guarantee, the
   shop assistant refused me a refund when I took it back.
   Considering that I know your store as one of the most reliable in
20   town, I am confident that you'll make also this customer satisfied
   by clarifying what I consider only a misunderstanding.

   If you are not able to make me a refund, then perhaps you could
   send me some gift vouchers to the same value as the present. I can
   then give them to my niece and this might compensate her
25   disappointment.

   Looking forward to your prompt response to this matter.

   Yours faithfully

   Gioia D'Amore

---

1   Has the writer included all the necessary information?
Look at the list of points needed in Exercise 2,
Content. Tick off all the ones that the writer has
included.

2   a) Has the writer copied from the question?
   b) Find and highlight two examples where the writer
has used her own words and put a tick (✓) next to
them.

3   a) In this letter there are three paragraphs which
consist of only one fairly short sentence. Look at
each one carefully and select the one which could
be included in another paragraph. Put brackets
around the sentence and use an arrow to indicate
which paragraph it could go to.
   b) Which paragraph could make use of the
expressions *Furthermore* … or *As well as* …?

4   Highlight the two occasions where the writer uses
flattery to attract the store manager's sympathy and
put a tick (✓) next to them.

5   Make the following corrections:
What change should be made to … *without any
doubts* in lines 6–7?
Which verb normally collocates with … *(someone) a
refund* in lines 17–18?
What preposition comes after *compensate …
(something)* in lines 24–25?

4 Now rewrite the answer making all the necessary
corrections.

UNIT 3 Getting to the top

READING

Part 3, Multiple choice

1 Read this article from a newspaper about people who leave things to the last minute and complete the following sentences. Use your own words as much as you can.

1 When the writer saw her friends getting on the train, she ....

2 Rupert left the train because ....

3 When thinking about Rupert and John, the writer ....

4 The writer considers her 'achievements' to be ....

5 The writer considers her mother ....

Strategy

In this type of multiple choice task, read the stem of the question and try to answer it by reading the relevant part of the text **before** looking at the four options.

No time like the last minute

Family Life

Mary Killen

AS I BOARDED the train at Paddington Station one night, I was delighted by the unexpected sight of three friends also boarding. 'Hurray!' we cried as we bagged a table for four in the dining car and settled down to the prospect of a delicious meal and stimulating conversation.

But with about three minutes to departure, I looked through the window to see one of our party wandering along the platform. 'Where's Rupert going?' I asked his wife. 'Oh, probably going to get a newspaper or something,' she shrugged. 'He likes to give himself these little thrills. He never actually boards a train until the whistle has actually blown.' Three agonising minutes after the train had started rolling down the tracks, Rupert came gasping back to the table, having just managed to get into the last carriage and walked all the way through the train.

Our friend Lucy's husband, John, derives a similar thrill from not arriving at airports at the stated latest check-in time. 'Even when we are there,' says Lucy, 'he carries on shopping after the flight is called and says, "Don't worry. Once you have checked in, it's OK. They always call out your actual name ."'

Rupert and John's penchant for 'competing' against time is unfortunately a vice I share. The thrill of 'just making' a train is addictive, and what is more depressing than hanging around a railway station or sitting in a motionless train? With life racing by so quickly, one wants to maximise every moment's potential.

Yet this is not the whole story. As a child I always walked through the school gate at the exact moment before I would be punished for being late, and experienced the thrill of triumph at having 'made it'. Now, in adult life, I find that each day holds the potential for a whole galaxy of bogus achievements of this nature. I never start packing for a holiday until an hour before we are due to set off. I never get my clothes ready for a party until twenty minutes before I have to leave home. I never send off my tax return until the last post on the day before it is due, even though it requires a thirty-minute drive to the nearest 7 p.m. collection box, when I could have posted it in my own village at 3.15 p.m.

Looking back, I realise the habit probably set in during adolescence, when I noted that my mother was always ready at least half an hour before she went out. On Tuesday nights when she set off to see friends, she used to be collected by car at 7.30 p.m. From 7 p.m., she would be pacing the garden. If she was giving a dinner party, she would have the table laid with cutlery the day before. Once she even said she could not see a long-lost cousin who wanted to drop in on December 9th because she would be 'too busy in the run-up to Christmas'.

We like to prove we can do things better than our parents, and therefore I stupidly window-shop in Oxford Street so that I have to take a taxi rather than a bus to Paddington Station, and arrive with my heart thumping. I cut it so fine when going to catch a train that, when I leave from home, I regularly have to finish getting dressed in the car on the way to the station. Old habits die hard but I'm beginning to see the advantages that might accrue from being ready in time. Think how much money I could save on taxis if I took buses in plenty of time instead. Think how much less panicky I would be at every party if I weren't doing up my buttons as I walked through the door. Think how much less anxious I would be if only I could be ready on time. One might even live longer without the stress of constantly competing against time.

With any luck my two little daughters will want to prove that they can do things better than I can and will take precisely the opposite line, deriving a thrill from being well-prepared, like both their grandmothers.

2 Now answer the multiple choice questions below by circling the best answer, **A**, **B**, **C** or **D**.

1   When the writer saw her friends getting on the train, she
    A   was worried that someone was missing.
    B   looked forward to a good trip.
    C   wondered why they were late.
    D   hoped they would find a table for four.

2   Why did Rupert leave the train?
    A   He had forgotten something important.
    B   He had changed his mind about the trip.
    C   His wife had asked him to get something.
    D   It was what he usually did.

3   When thinking about Rupert and John, the writer
    A   appreciates why they act as they do.
    B   is depressed by their behaviour.
    C   is determined to make better use of her time.
    D   realises the potential dangers of their behaviour.

4   The writer considers her 'achievements' to be
    A   worthwhile.
    B   illusory.
    C   childish.
    D   a sign of boredom.

5   The writer considers that her mother
    A   set a bad example.
    B   controlled her own anxiety.
    C   was inhospitable to relatives.
    D   provided a model to react against.

6   What does the writer hope for her own daughters?
    A   They will have better lives than her.
    B   They will not be influenced by family members.
    C   They will trust to luck.
    D   They will not follow her example.

3 Underline the two- or three-word combinations in the article that mean the same as the following.

Example: a statement which declares your income for the year (*para 5*) = *a tax return*

1   something that you don't expect to see (*para 1*)
2   talk that is very interesting (*para 1*)
3   an occasion where friends are invited around to your house for a meal (*para 6*)
4   a relative that you haven't seen for a long time (*para 6*)
5   to look without buying (*para 7*)

4 Look at the words in Column **B** and find a word from Column **A** with which they collocate. Each word in Column **B** is used twice.

A	B	
golden	research	1 ....
body of	evidence	2 ....
concrete	opportunity	3 ....
missed	situation	4 ....
current		5 ....
market		6 ....
social		7 ....
solid		8 ....

5 Use appropriate word combinations from Exercise 4 to complete the following sentences.

1   The company needs to carry out extensive .... before it develops any new products.
2   Don't allow this .... to slip through your fingers. You may never have the chance again!
3   Whilst the .... looks very gloomy we are able to predict much brighter long-term prospects.
4   The police didn't have any .... that the woman was present at the scene of the crime so she was released without being charged. (*2 possibilities*)
5   There is a growing .... which suggests that many species of birds are dying out.
6   Sam is really quite shy and finds herself getting anxious in any .... like a party or evening out with friends.
7   It's a pity you didn't take the job. That's a real ....

VOCABULARY

Expressions to do with achievement and success

1 Use one of the idiomatic expressions A–F in the correct form to complete sentences 1–5. The meaning is given in brackets. There is an extra expression you do not need.

A   make a go of
B   make one's mark
C   rise to the top
D   come out right
E   go according to plan
F   make it

1   Melissa has always dreamed of a career in films. It's hard to believe she's finally .... (*succeeded*).
2   Most people find their careers .... (*progress smoothly*) until the age of 30 when they begin to get restless.
3   Patrick knew that he would have to .... (*impress people*) early on in his career if he was going to chair the company one day.
4   After a somewhat difficult start, Catrin is finally .... (*being successful*) her software business.
5   By the time Graham was 25 he wanted to be able to .... (*achieve one's ambition*) of his profession.

Phrasal verbs and idioms

2 Look at each of the expressions in the chart below and use your dictionary to find out the necessary information. The first one has been done as an example.

	has an object	is an idiom
come up with	✓	
get off (the ground)		
get ahead		
pass over		
get off (to a flying start)		
pull off		
carry out		
pay off		

Tip: When you are recording phrasal verbs it is important to remember whether they occur with an object or not. A good dictionary will give you this information.

3 Replace the word(s) in brackets in each of the sentences below with an appropriate phrasal verb or idiom from the chart in Exercise 2.

1   The race is on amongst the pharmaceutical companies to .... (*discover*) a cure for cancer.
2   Women in the workplace are finding out that competing with men has finally .... (*been worthwhile*)– more women than men were promoted last year in the service industries.
3   Managers have realised that the quickest way to be .... (*successful in their career*) is to have a team of dedicated staff around them.
4   Both doctors and patients have criticised a plan which would allow nurses to .... (*undertake*) more medical work.
5   Sales of George Michael's latest album have .... (*been very high since the beginning*). (*Clue: This is an idiom.*)
6   Nobody expected Howard Marks to .... (*succeed in doing*) the deal once again.
7   A lack of money is the usual reason that small businesses fail to be .... (*successful in the first place*). (*Clue: This is an idiom.*)
8   Don't be upset if you are .... (*not chosen*) the first time you apply for promotion – it usually pays to be persistent in these matters.

Prepositions (CB page 37)

4 Complete each sentence using an appropriate preposition.

1   When Gordon had his fortieth birthday he decided it was time to *take stock* .... *his life* so far.
2   It's no good sitting there *feeling sorry* .... *yourself!* You need to try and make an effort to cheer up.
3   Be careful! A lot of people have *gambled* .... making money on the Stock Market and lost everything.
4   Many Western diseases are *associated* .... a diet that is too high in fat and sugar.

5   After Simon and Lucille became engaged all their
    thoughts were *focused* .... the day they would be
    getting married.

6   Barry is very keen to *pursue his interest* ....
    photography.

7   When Danny *looked back* .... *his life* he found to
    his surprise that he didn't have any regrets.

8   We regret the cancellation of tonight's performance;
    this is due to events .... *our control*.

Tip: Try to learn the whole expression in italics,
e.g. *pursue an interest in something*.

ENGLISH IN USE
Part 3, Error correction

1 Some but not all of the lines in the following text
contain one extra word that should not be there. Read
the text straight through to find out what it's about.
Then <u>underline</u> the unnecessary words and tick (✓)
the lines that are correct. The exercise begins with
two examples (**0**).

COFFEE REPUBLIC

0   I'd been a lawyer in London for five years <u>and</u> when I realised

0 ✓   it wasn't for me. Not knowing quite what to do, I packed a

1   bag and travelled around of the world. While I was in New York

2   I'd start up the day in a coffee bar where I'd have a low-fat coffee

3   and cake and it would keep me going for the whole day. When

4   I came back to London there didn't seem to be any such coffee

5   bars that were like the ones in New York, and after doing some

6   market research I realised there was a gap in the market for this

7   type of the coffee bar. I wanted to be the one to fill it. I had the drive

8   and ambition but no capital to put the business off into action. I had

9   meetings with a number of bank managers, who would listen but

10   it was such a new idea that nobody believed <u>in</u> it would work.

11   Finally, after 20 bank managers I found one who <u>he</u> shared my

12   vision. Exactly one year later on I opened the first Coffee Republic

13   in London. All that hard work has paid it off. We're now a public

14   company with 34 stores in England and growing. Each morning

15   I make a time to visit a Coffee Republic and look around at

16   my dream come to life right here in the centre of London.

---

2 How many times did the following grammatical errors appear in the text?
Write down the line numbers next to each category.

incorrect use of a preposition ....

incorrect use of an article ....

unnecessary use of a pronoun in a relative clause ....

incorrect use of a pronoun in a phrasal verb ....

unnecessary use of a determiner ....

LANGUAGE STUDY

Wish/If only (CB page 34)

1 Identify which of the following sentences refer to the present and which to the past. Complete the sentences using the correct tense of the verbs in brackets.

1 I wish I .... (*learn*) to swim when I was younger.

2 If only the trains .... (*be*) more reliable.

3 I wish I .... (*do*) more revision for this exam.

4 If only we .... (*have*) more time to do the things we want to do.

2 Rewrite the following sentences using *wish* or *if only*.

Example: The car broke down so we missed the film.
   I wish the car hadn't broken down.

1 It is a shame you don't live closer.

2 I can't read as often as I'd like to.

3 I always regretted not taking up his offer.

4 I'd have preferred the film to be shorter.

5 We can't go to the beach, the weather's terrible.

6 I've got an awful stomachache. I shouldn't have eaten so much.

7 I overslept and missed the appointment.

8 I forgot to send Michael a birthday card.

3 Complete the following sentences using a form of *would* where possible and *do* elsewhere.

1 I wish I .... smoke. It's costing me a fortune.

2 I wish Peter .... smoke when we're eating.

3 I wish you .... keep tapping your fingers.

4 If only I .... bite my nails.

5 If only my car .... start more easily.

6 I wish my car .... cost so much money to run.

7 He often wishes he .... waste so much time watching TV.

8 I wish you .... turn that TV off. I'm trying to read.

Conditionals/mixed conditionals (CB page 35)

4 Some but not all of the following sentences contain mistakes. Correct those that are wrong. Check your answers by looking at Coursebook page 201.

1 Whenever I lie in bed too long I will get a headache.

2 I'll lend you the car provided you fill it with petrol.

3 Unless you would have told me, I'd never have known you were 40!

4 I wouldn't do that if I had been you.

5 If it hadn't have been for that last question I might never have failed.

6 They'll never win provided they strengthen their defence.

7 If I'd kept up my Spanish I could apply for this job.

8 If I had followed your directions we wouldn't have been lost now.

5 Complete the following paragraphs with the correct form of the verbs in brackets.

1 If my dad .... (*not decide*) to go on holiday to Tunisia he .... (*not meet*) my mum, which means I .... (*not be born*) and I .... (*write*) this now!

2 If I .... (*be*) better at maths at school I .... (*take*) more of an interest in my studies. Unfortunately I got bored and left. If I .... (*stay on*) and .... (*pass*) my exams I .... (*have*) a better job now.

3 My friend Cathy almost certainly .... (*not be*) a lawyer now if her first serious boyfriend .... (*not break*) her heart and .... (*leave*) her for her best friend. She met someone else who was studying at university and later decided to study law.

4 If I .... (*not spend*) all my summer holidays sunbathing, my skin .... (*be*) in much better condition now.

5 If my father's car .... (*not be stolen*) he .... (*not ask*) his colleague to give him a lift. Consequently he .... (*become*) involved in a discussion about playing the lottery, and .... (*not decide*) to buy a ticket that weekend. One thing's for sure, if he .... (*not buy*) that ticket I .... (*not drive*) around in this beautiful Mercedes!

ENGLISH IN USE

Part 6, Discourse cloze (CB page 41)

1 Read the following text and then choose from the list (**A–J**) the phrase which best fits each of the spaces (**1–6**). Some of the suggested answers do not fit at all. The exercise begins with an example (**0**).

If you would like some help with this task, go to Exercise 2 below first.

Getting things done

We all want to sail through life without anxiety, frustration or fear. But life isn't like that. If we make our lives too comfortable, always avoiding unpleasant tasks, (**0**) ..J.. . Because for one thing, those nasty, unpleasant jobs don't go away when (**1**) .... . For another, whenever we try to avoid initial discomfort, we start to hate and fear anxieties and (**2**) .... . If we don't go to the dentist with a slight toothache, we may end up suffering agonising pain. We all know this and (**3**) .... . But how can we get ourselves into a positive frame of mind? We have to tell ourselves that we can stand the initial discomfort involved in doing a task right away. Although we may not like it, (**4**) .... . If we fear too much, we may end up restricting our lives to such an extent that eventually (**5**) .... . When we tell ourselves we can't stand failing or being unpopular, we take even fewer risks and achieve even less. We can escape from these negative feelings if (**6**) .... . If, for example, we have a 5,000 word essay to write, we may not start at all because it is too daunting. But if we give ourselves ten minutes at the desk, we can at least make a start. Then we have already diminished the problem.

A   we make our wishes known
B   we experience no excitement and joy because we fear risk and anxiety so much
C   we know people may dislike us
D   we must give ourselves a reward for doing them
E   we become increasingly less able to cope with these feelings
F   we don't like being told
G   we can bear it
H   we break up difficult tasks into manageable chunks
I   we don't do them
J   we end up causing ourselves more discomfort and anxiety

2 Use the following hints to help you choose the correct extract.

1 Find a pronoun in one of the extracts that refers to 'unpleasant jobs'.
2 Suffering more pain through not going to the dentist is an example of what?
3 If you already know something, you might feel this is unnecessary.
4 'Although' indicates a change from positive to negative in this sentence.
5 This is a result of 'restricting our lives' too much.
6 'give ourselves ten minutes at the desk' is an example of what?

WRITING
Part 1, Formal letter (CB pages 42/43)

1 Read this writing task.

For the last two weeks you have had a holiday job in a restaurant. Your contract lasts another four weeks, but you are unhappy with the job and wish to leave immediately. Read the notes that you have made on your job description and the letter you have recently sent to a friend. Using this information carefully, write a **letter** to your boss, Mr Franks, explaining that you would like to leave and requesting a reference.

Dear Jan

Taking this job was the biggest mistake of my life. The hours are much longer than I expected, the work is exhausting and the guests are so rude! The problem is that I'm supposed to give my boss two weeks at least to find someone else. What are my chances of getting a reference from him if I walk out now?

Terms and conditions for post of waiter/waitress

1 Hours of work: 12.30–3 p.m. and 7–11 p.m. Punctuality is expected.

we don't finish before midnight!

2. Full uniform is provided and you are expected to look smart at all times.

yes, but have to wash and iron it myself

3. You must give two weeks notice if you wish to terminate your contract.

unfair for a six-week contract

2 Read the mark scheme for the task. This will tell you what the examiner is looking for in an ideal answer.

Content (points covered): the letter must include the following:
- that you wish to leave your job immediately
- the reasons for handing in your notice (longer hours than in contract; rudeness of the guests; lack of more than one uniform)
- request for a reference from Mr Franks.

Organisation and cohesion: the letter should be organised into clear paragraphs devoted to each of the above points.

Range: the letter must use appropriate tenses (e.g. present perfect for describing the situation up to now); the language of explanation, and for expressing regret (CB page 34); language of polite requests (for the reference).

Register: fairly formal. The tone must be polite and apologetic and try to explain the problems tactfully.

Target reader: Mr Franks would consider letting you leave immediately and be prepared to write a reference.

Accuracy: should not contain major errors that lead to misunderstandings or have a negative effect on the reader.

3 Now read this answer and do the questions below.

Dear Mr Franks,

I am sorry to inform you that I wish to resign from my post as waitress at your restaurant.

I have been employed as a waitress in your restaurant for the past two weeks. However, I have decided to leave because the hours are much longer than I expected. I am often asked to work overtime which is unpaid; the work is very tiring. I have been allocated many additional tasks which did not appear in my job description; I also find it very difficult to deal with customers who are rude to me. Additionally, though I have been provided with a uniform, I am required to wash and iron it myself. I find this difficult to do as I have only been provided with one uniform and it is not always possible to wash and dry it before the next day.

As I have only been employed on a six-week contract, I would be pleased if I could leave immediately without giving the required two weeks notice. Also I would be very grateful if you could provide me with a reference.

I am sorry for any inconvenience that this may cause and I look forward to hearing from you soon.

Yours sincerely

Sally

---

1 Look at the list of points needed in Exercise 2, **Content**. Tick off all the ones that the writer has included. You must include all the content points to score more than 2 in the exam.

2 a) Find an example in paragraph 2 where the writer has used the same words as the input. Rewrite this part.
   b) Find and highlight three examples where the writer has rephrased the input notes, and put a tick (✓) next to them.

3 Look at the punctuation in the section 'However, I have decided to leave ... customers who are rude to me.' in paragraph 2. What changes could be made? Rewrite this section to include clearer punctuation and the expressions *Furthermore* ... or *Moreover* ... .

4 a) Study the writer's use of the passive as opposed to the active in paragraph 2, e.g. *I am often asked to work overtime* ... . Is this likely to have a negative or positive effect on Mr Franks?
   b) What fixed expression does the writer use to begin the letter? What two expressions does she use to make polite requests in paragraph 3? Highlight all of these and put a tick (✓) next to them.

5 The letter is very nicely written but a little on the short side. Add two more sentences to the end of paragraph 3 (after '... if you could provide me with a reference').

4 Now rewrite the answer making all the necessary additions.

Amusing yourself

READING

Part 1, Multiple matching

1 Read the magazine article on page 29. Match each statement (1–13) with the person (A–D) in the text to whom it refers.

Strategy

Look back at Unit 1 (page 4). What is the first reading strategy you should adopt for this type of question?
a) skim read the text quickly?
b) read the text through very carefully?

Which person or people

has conducted an analysis of how fans behave and why?	**1**	
works in a place where a series was filmed?	**2**	
thinks there is some justification for the stereotype of a typical fan?	**3**	**A** Max Hora
thinks programme-makers despise their audience?	**4**	
focuses his collecting on one particular area?	**5**	**B** Matt Bielby
thinks fans are unfairly labelled?	**6** **7**	
is responsible for getting information to fans?	**8** **9**	**C** David Howe
says that technology provides more opportunities for fans?	**10**	
is unappreciative of some objects connected with cult TV series?	**11**	**D** Henry Jenkins
recognises that a place has become popular because of a series?	**12**	
works in publishing?	**13**	

2

1 In paragraph 1 of the text we have a number of words to do with television programmes. Look at the following clues and see if you can remember what the words are.

1 .... : a single programme in a series
2 .... : the people that the actors play in a programme
3 .... : producers and directors
4 .... : storylines

2 Now complete this text with the appropriate word.

When will (1) .... wake up to the needs of their audiences? I recently watched the new soap opera on Channel 4. How could anyone begin to believe such a far-fetched (2) .... ? Two murders, an affair between an old woman and a young boy and someone who wins the lottery, and all this in the first (3) .... ! And as for the (4) .... ; these people seem to have no resemblance whatsoever to the kind of people we would expect to meet in such a situation.

LIVING IN A TV TIMEWARP

Everyone has a favourite television programme, but they tend not to record and re-watch every episode, endlessly discuss the plots, dress up as the characters at conventions, collect every available item of merchandise and engage in passionate letter-writing campaigns with the programme-makers. These are all typical activities for fans from the extraordinarily obsessive world of cult TV.

There are two main kinds of programme that attract this kind of following: science fiction and fantasy drama. The fact that a programme is no longer made may add to its appeal. Max Hora works in 'The Prisoner' shop at the Portmeirion Village Hotel in Wales, the distinctive location of the cult TV series 'The Prisoner', starring Patrick McGoohan. He also helps run 'The Prisoner' fan club, 'Six of One', which boasts 2,000 members, little short of incredible given that not a single episode has been made since 1968. 'Some 250,000 people visit Portmeirion every year,' he says proudly. 'And I'd say that about half of those come because of "The Prisoner"'. But the cult shows to end all cult shows are the science-fiction epics 'Star Trek' and 'Dr Who'.

David Howe is one of the country's leading authorities on 'Dr Who' and one of its biggest fans. More than a thousand items have been marketed in conjunction with the programme, and he's got one example of almost all of them. The main part of his collection consists of books. He has a copy of every one of the one hundred and fifty-three published. In most cases, he has got every cover, edition and printing. All in mint condition, of course. Howe points out just how normal the average 'Dr Who' fan is: 'He's between twenty and thirty years old, well-adjusted, married with children, plays tennis or something in the evening,

drives a car and might watch the odd 'Dr Who' episode on video if he hasn't got anything better to do.'

So how accurate is the 'anorak' stereotype these fans get labelled with? Matt Bielby, editor of the science-fiction magazine 'SFX', concedes that it may have a factual basis. 'A lot of the most excessive fans are male, have studied physics or engineering and wear a rather unappealing combination of ill-fitting T-shirts, nasty jeans and horrible badges relating to their favourite programmes – and anoraks. But they're the hard core, the ones who buy all the tacky commercial merchandise. Most fans are perfectly ordinary people. They come in both sexes and all ages'.

A fanatical passion for science-fiction or fantasy TV does not fit with the traditional psychiatric diagnosis of obsessive and compulsive behaviour. A wider explanation is provided in a definitive scientific discussion of fan culture, 'Science Fiction Audiences: Watching Dr Who and Star Trek', by John Tulloch and Henry Jenkins.

According to Jenkins, Director of Film and Media Studies at the Massachusetts Institute of Technology, 'Fans are often seen as emotionally uncontrollable, obsessed with consumption and trivia, socially isolated and incapable of separating fiction from real life.' Jenkins proposes that the media perpetuate these myths for a reason. Given that statistics tell us that most households indiscriminately watch eight or so hours of TV every day, he argues, 'It is useful to have an image of someone who is really obsessed with television – a fan – so that your own relationship with the media can be presented as normal, sane and rational. Secondly, it fits the contempt which the media industry has towards its own product, a sense that if these people actually find something of value in television, then there must be something wrong with them.' Jenkins identifies several elements that all cult programmes seem to share: 'A densely-constructed world which rewards re-reading and speculation, an element of the idiosyncratic (either in style or content), plus a strong image of community or friendship which may often become a model for the behaviour of groups of fans themselves.' The conclusion is that these universal aspects appeal to a wide selection of people, like a kind of modern folklore. Fans claim these programmes as myths that belong to everyone, like Robin Hood and King Arthur. With today's sophisticated technology, viewers are not content merely to sit around talking but can join in, poaching characters and concepts to convey their own ideas. 'When I first started,' Jenkins recalls, 'we made audio-tapes of 'Star Trek' episodes, and then produced fanzines on office mimeograph machines. Today we can videotape shows and send stories and criticism via the Internet. We can re-edit video-footage to create whole new home-made versions of the programmes.'

anorak = someone who has an obsessive interest in a hobby (slang).

3 Look at the text again and circle all the words to do with: kinds of programme (*para 2*)
books (*para 3*)

VOCABULARY

Homophones (CB page 45)

1 Underline the correct word in each pair of words.

1 Do you fancy a game of *drafts/draughts* – it's a lot easier than chess!

2 After five days of play the cricket match ended in a *draw/drawer*.

3 I like to *browse/brows* around art galleries in my spare time. I'm particularly fond of oil on *canvas/canvass*.

4 This computer game comes on a single floppy *disc/disk* and only takes up five *kilobites/kilobytes* of space.

5 Monopoly is probably one of the best-selling *bored/board* games of all time.

6 Theresa plays the *base/bass* guitar in a rock *band/banned* at weekends.

7 In the book 'Rebecca' the *heroin/heroine* of the story is the second wife of Max de Winter.

8 *Martial/Marshall* arts are an excellent form of self-defence.

9 The final *seen/scene* in the film 'Seven' is truly unforgettable.

10 In the warmer weather we like to go to *fêtes/fates* and other outdoor festivals.

Word formation *in-* and *-less* (CB page 48)

2 Use the words in the box to complete the sentences below using the affix indicated.

famous	harm	audible	count	thought
secure	age	capable	power	different

Words formed with *in-*

1 Felix is feeling very .... about his relationship with his girlfriend Sally – he thinks she may be seeing another man.

2 The fans of the opposing football team found it difficult to forgive the .... kicking incident of ten years ago.

3 Clive found it impossible to remain .... to the plight of the refugees.

4 The president is incompetent and appears to be .... of doing his job properly.

5 I would have enjoyed the play were it not for the fact that the lead actor spoke in an almost .... voice. I could hardly hear him.

Words formed with *-less*

6 It was pretty .... of you to forget your mother's birthday.

7 Much as the government wanted to, it was .... to intervene in the crisis.

8 The plot of that book was hardly original; in fact it's been done .... times before.

9 Good clothes should never go out of fashion – they should be.................... .

10 Although my boss looks quite intimidating he's fairly .... in reality.

3 In which of the sentences above does the affix *in-* or *-less* not indicate a negative meaning of the adjective? Write the number of the sentences here ....

Expressions to do with laughter

4 In each sentence underline the appropriate word. The first one appeared on page 49 of the Coursebook.

1 I tried to *keep/hold/maintain* a straight face but I couldn't help laughing.

2 When I heard the news I just had to chuckle *by/to/with* myself. I was so amused.

3 The actor had such a strange voice that her audience just *melted/dissolved/fell* into laughter every time she spoke.

4 Like everyone else in the audience I fell *about/out/through* laughing when the singer tripped over his microphone.

5 None of the jokes in my after-dinner speech *lifted/rose/raised* a laugh from the audience.

6 He laughed his *top/ears/head* off during the film.

7 At school I used to get the *giggles/laughs/titters* whenever I was told off.

8 People usually laugh *at/to/with* my accent whenever I try and speak Spanish.

ENGLISH IN USE
Part 5, Word formation

1. Complete the following sentences with the correct form of the words in CAPITALS. All the words you need are nouns.

1 We're having a .... for charity. Would you care to donate some money? COLLECT.

2 The young man could give the police no .... of why he had stolen the car. EXPLAIN

3 I thought their last .... of Romeo and Juliet was rather poor. PRODUCE

4 If you're not able to collect your order we can make a .... tomorrow. DELIVER

5 The .... of the plane is a mystery. It seemed to vanish into thin air. APPEAR

6 What are the latest .... in the murder enquiry? DEVELOP

7 There is a popular .... that all snakes are poisonous. But it's not true. CONCEPT

8 The car factory will have to close unless the company increases its .... in new machinery. INVEST

Tip: When you're recording nouns made from verbs remember to make a note of which ones have a plural form.

2 Complete the following sentences with the correct form of the words in CAPITALS. All the words you need are adjectives.

1 That's a rather exquisitely .... tablecloth. PATTERN

2 I always feel rather .... at the end of the year. SENTIMENT

3 Isn't it funny how some fashions never date and seem to be .... ? TIME

4 Eating that meat could be .... It looks .... to me. DANGER/COOK

5 It costs a .... amount of money to keep up-to-date with technology. CONSIDER

6 Swimming can be one of the most .... forms of exercise. BENEFIT

7 If you're not more .... in class you won't pass your exams. ATTEND

8 His .... death at the age of only 39 shocked his whole family. TIME

3 Read the texts opposite. Use the words in the box to form one word that fits in the same numbered space in the text. The exercise begins with an example (**0**).

THE REAL ROBINSON CRUSOE

In the early (**0**) ....*eighteenth*.... century, Alexander Selkirk was a member of the crew of a small British ship which was sailing on a voyage of (**1**) .... . He had a habit of telling jokes all the time, hundreds of them every day. At first, there was plenty of (**2**) .... on board but soon the other sailors began to show signs of (**3**) .... at Selkirk's non-stop joke-telling, which they had ceased to find (**4**) .... . Off the coast of Chile, they abandoned him on an (**5**) .... island. Selkirk stayed there alone for seven years until he was rescued by a ship that accidentally stopped at the island to get fresh water. He had not found a (**6**) .... treasure hidden by pirates and having had no-one to talk to, he had lost the power of (**7**) .... .

(**0**)	**EIGHT**	(**4**)	HUMOUR
		(**5**)	INHABIT
(**1**)	DISCOVER	(**6**)	PRICE
(**2**)	LAUGH	(**7**)	SPEAK
(**3**)	IRRITATE		

THE RED PARROT THEATRE

Does the idea of watching another video at home fill you with a sense of (**8**) .... ? Are you tired of computer games? Fed up with dull, (**9**) .... television programmes? Why not try a different form of (**10**) .... ? You can't beat the thrill of watching a live (**11**) .... and 'The Red Parrot Theatre' is offering a number of special (**12**) .... on tickets for its new programme of plays, which includes both (**13**) .... drama and works by contemporary writers. There's plenty of (**14**) .... , including comedy, tragedy and musicals. There is something for everyone and prices are very (**15**) .... . Phone the box office for further information.

(**8**)	BORE	(**12**)	REDUCE
(**9**)	INTEREST	(**13**)	TRADITION
(**10**)	ENTERTAIN	(**14**)	VARY
(**11**)	PERFORM	(**15**)	REASON

LANGUAGE STUDY

Gerunds and infinitives (CB pages 50/51)

1 Rewrite the sentences replacing the words in *italics* with the word in CAPITALS and one of the following prepositions from the box. Your answer must contain a gerund form!

with	for	of	in	on	about

Example: I'm really *pleased with myself that I passed* the test. PROUD

I'm really proud of myself for passing the test.

1 I feel really *ashamed that I forgot* his birthday. GUILTY

2 There *isn't the faintest possibility that you can win* the lottery. CHANCE

3 He *is known to lose* his temper easily. REPUTATION

4 There is *really nothing better than to eat* a healthy diet. SUBSTITUTE

5 I don't *think we should make* people do military service. BELIEVE

6 She *tried to answer* the most difficult questions first. CONCENTRATED

7 He *has to check* every lock in the house when he leaves. OBSESSED

8 The students *complained that they had* to do so much homework. PROTESTED

2 <u>Underline</u> the correct verb forms in the following paragraphs.

1 OK everyone. Can I have your attention? I'd like to start by talking about the recent meeting and then go on (1) *to examine/examining* last year's sales figures. If you can stop (2) *to talk/talking* just for a minute perhaps we can start.

2 Poor Rob can't seem to remember (3) *to make/making* a fool of himself at the party. I told him how everybody had asked him to be quiet but he just went on (4) *to sing/singing*. He said he's going to really try (5) *to behave/behaving* himself more in future.

3 I was driving along Warwick Road and stopped (6) *to buy/buying* a newspaper. Unfortunately, I didn't remember (7) *to indicate/indicating* and the man behind hit me. I forgot (8) *to take/taking* his number which is a pity because he now denies being involved.

3 Complete the following text putting the verbs in brackets into the correct form, gerund or *to-* infinitive.

Since our daughter was born I've realised how much I enjoy (1) .... (be) a father. Before she came along, people kept (2) .... (tell) me that being a parent would be really hard work and some even suggested (3) .... (put off) the decision to have children for a few more years.

However, I decided (4) .... (follow) my instincts and go for it. I admit (5) .... (not get) much sleep has been really hard and I miss (6) .... (go) out with my friends as often as I used to. In fact, I find it difficult to recollect (7) .... (be) able to go out whenever I felt like it.

Despite this, I can't imagine (8) .... (not have) her around. She never fails (9) .... (make) me smile when I first see her every morning and I never realised (10) .... (see) a toddler develop would be so interesting.

Modifying adverbs and adjectives (CB page 52)

4 <u>Underline</u> the correct modifier in the following sentences.

1 There's *little/a little* bit of milk left if you want a cup of tea.

2 I'm so bored. There's *little/a little* in the way of entertainment, isn't there?

3 I was *rather/fairly* disappointed to hear you can't attend the Open Day.

4 The weather's *rather/fairly* good, but I wish it was a little warmer.

5 I'm *fairly/virtually* finished if you can wait just one more minute.

6 I'm *absolutely/extremely* grateful for all your help.

7 I'm very interested *certainly/indeed*. Tell me more.

8 He's *quite/a quite* nice, isn't he?

ENGLISH IN USE
Part 3, Error correction (CB page 55)

1 The error correction exercise in the exam could contain mistakes in punctuation and spelling. Correct the following sentences under each category. You can refer to the Coursebook pages 212 and 213 to help you.

1 Capitals
1 i'm going to visit john in london in may.
2 the principal will be meeting some russian visitors on monday morning.

2 Full stops and question marks
1 Tomorrow should turn out fine However, cold winds are expected. from the North
2 You could go on a diet Alternatively have you thought about taking up exercise

3 Commas
1 Although the weather was bad we had a great time.
2 This is Sarah who started with us yesterday.
3 This contract, which runs out soon is not expected to be renewed.
4 We're going to Italy Spain and then China if we can get a visa that is.

4 Commas and quotation marks in indirect speech
1 Andrea Terry said. Have you seen my umbrella?
2 Anyway, we'd better be leaving said Karen. It's getting late.

5 Apostrophes
1 Steves borrowing his dads car for the weekend.
2 During the 1960s he led many of the students demonstration's

6 Hyphens in compounds
1 I bumped into my ex boyfriend last Saturday in the car-park.
2 She's got a beautiful three year old daughter.

2 In most of the lines in the following letter there is either a spelling or punctuation error. Write the correctly spelled word or show the correct punctuation. If there is no mistake in a line, put a tick (✓). The exercise begins with three examples (**0**).

Tip: Read the text through once. Then read each line again from right to left to focus your attention on each word rather than on meaning.

0	*it's*	I know its been such a long time since I wrote to you.
0	*here*	Anyway, I arrived <u>hear</u> on the 20th and started my course last
0	✓	week. I've met lots of people from all over the world and I think
1	....	its a really good language school. Our teacher has just shown
2	....	us a Mr Bean video. It was hilarious. Have you ever seen any of
3	....	them. In this one he's decided to decorate the living room but his
4	....	paint brush is stiff and unusable. So he wraps everything in the
5	....	room in newspaper – I mean everything, right down to each
6	....	individual grape in the fruit bowl. He then puts a fire-work in the
7	....	tin of paint and goes to run out of the room. There's a great
8	....	moment when he can't open the door because the handle which
9	....	always comes of and which he keeps in the fruit bowl, is wrapped
10	....	up in newspaper along with everything else. He finally finds the
11	....	handle and gets out. Prior too all this Mr Bean had had a visitor.
12	....	Well, this man had forgoten to take his hat and he enters the living
13	....	room just as the explosion happens. The final seen is a view of the
14	....	beautifuly painted room with a silhouette of the man reaching out to
15	....	take his hat. It probably isn't quiet as funny when I describe it but if
16	....	you get the chance to see it …

WRITING

Part 2, Article (CB pages 54/55)

1 Read this writing task.

> An English language magazine is interested in the forms of exercise that young people do in different countries. The editor has asked people from around the world to write in and tell other readers about the most popular sporting activities in their own country. Write the **article**. (Write approximately 250 words.)

2 Read the mark scheme for the task. This will tell you what the examiner is looking for in an ideal answer.

> **Content (points covered):** the article must state clearly which country is being written about; should mention three to four sporting activities; may give reasons for the popularity of each sport; may discuss the history of each sport.
>
> **Organisation and cohesion:** the article should be divided into clear paragraphs (e.g. one paragraph for each sport), with the use of subheadings where appropriate, e.g.
>
> > paragraph 1 – introduction
> > paragraphs 2/3/(4) – description of each sport/reasons for popularity/history
> > paragraph 5 – conclusion
>
> **Range:** should use language of description (e.g. present tense for habits and routines – *In the UK many young people play tennis in the summer*) and explanation (*One of the reasons for the popularity of cycling is ...*).
>
> **Register:** semi-formal. Should aim to be friendly in tone to appeal to the reader of the magazine.
>
> **Target reader:** would be informed about the sports in that particular country.
>
> **Accuracy:** should not contain major errors that lead to misunderstandings or have a negative effect on the reader.

3 Now read the answer on page 35 and do the questions below.

1. a) Look at the list of points needed in Exercise 2 **Content**. Put a tick (✓) against the points that are covered.
   b) Is there any area that needs to be covered in more detail? Put a line through any information that is not really relevant (Is the reader of the article really interested in the writer's own habits?) and use the (⌐) symbol to indicate where you would add extra information.

2. a) Has the writer organised the article appropriately?
   b) What headings could the writer have used for each paragraph to catch the reader's attention?
   c) Find two occasions where the writer makes a punctuation error in the sentences beginning with *Perhaps* ... .
   d) Highlight the other linking phrases and check that they are used appropriately.

3. a) What tense would sound more natural in the opening sentence?
   b) What tense would be more appropriate in paragraph 3, *In the Olympics* ... ?

4. Find the following errors and make the necessary corrections:
   ... many varieties of exercises ... (*para 1*)
   incorrect collocations with ... *sports* (*para 2*)
   incorrect modifying adjective ... *only a little choice* (*para 2*)

4 Now write your own answer to the question.

Sporting Hong Kong

1 Nowadays, young people are taking part in many varieties of exercises than ever before. Perhaps, the most important consideration when choosing a sport is to look at what kind of sport you are interested in, and more importantly, the sports services available in your area or country. For instance, if your hobby is swimming, and your region has not got a swimming pool, then in reality, you can forget that kind of sport.

2 In my home country, Hong Kong, which is a small city, the varieties of sport activities are few compared with those in big countries, for example, the USA. Therefore, young people have only a little choice in choosing the sport for them. But if there are choices they are mostly 'inside sports' and not 'outside sports', for example, American Football and Cricket. However, indeed, as it should be, there are still some sports which are well known and popular. For instance, Table Tennis and Badminton.

3 In my opinion, the most popular sporting activity for young people in Hong Kong is Badminton. In the Olympics the Chinese won several gold, silver and bronze medals in this sport for their country. Perhaps, this is the reason why young people in Hong Kong choose this sport as their favourite one.

4 As regards myself, I play a lot of Badminton in my spare time. There are a lot of things which I really like about this sport, for example, I like the pace and energy of the game. In addition, I really like the challenging nature of the game and the various techniques used for playing this sport.

READING

Part 3, Multiple choice

1 Read this newspaper article about a musician and answer the multiple choice questions on page 37 by circling the best answer, **A, B, C** or **D**.

Strategy

Do you remember which strategy you used in Unit 3 for multiple choice questions? Try it again before you start question 1. (See page 20.)

Sally Beamish – Composer

WHAT DO YOU DO if you get robbed? Take up composing? In the case of Sally Beamish, definitely. The thief has never been caught and her viola and video-player have never been recovered.

The robbery took place in London, where she was very active as a freelance player. Six months earlier, she had composed music for a set of six poems by Irina Ratushinskaya. This strengthened Beamish in her belief in herself as a composer. The shock of the theft of the invaluable 1747 Gabriella viola, which was not even her own but on loan, finally set the seal on her decision to leave the urban stress of London and head for the country of her husband, Scotland, and begin a new life.

Sally Beamish was born in 1956 into a musical family. She could write musical notes before she could write the letters of the alphabet. At the age of seven, she wrote an opera, or 'opra' as she called it then, based on a story she had read. Her grandmother taught her to sight-read music at the piano, but it was her mother who encouraged (and later discouraged) her interest in the violin, leading Sally, at fifteen, to take up the viola. Living in North London, she mucked in with a precocious band of chamber music players, as one of those useful musicians that could turn their hand proficiently to the violin, viola or piano.

At the Royal Northern College of Music, the Principal recommended that she attend the musical composition course given by Anthony Gilbert. Gilbert suggested that, as an already experienced composer, she should go her own way. But this was not easy for her. Her work bore no relation to what was then fashionable. I didn't have the confidence to realise that what I was doing was just as valid.'

Beamish stopped composing. She became a busy viola player. She now recognises this period as a very unhappy one when, despite her talent as a performer, she had nothing special to say. A chance encounter with the Scottish composer, Martin Dalby, proved to be a turning point for her. Looking at the music she had written, he encouraged her to believe once again that she could be a composer. However, it was not until two years later that she received her first professional commission. Her panic was so great that when she came to attend the final rehearsal of *Dances and Nocturnes*, she took out her pen and made an attempt, resisted by the performers, to cut out several bars of music, out of fear that her music would not be regarded as professional. Later, Beamish entered a work for a competition. She didn't win but afterwards she met the composer, Oliver Knussen, who remembered the work. She acknowledges the invaluable help Knussen gave her, discussing her compositions and crises of confidence. Her composition *No, I Am Not Afraid*, received its first performance six months before her viola was stolen. Shortly after the robbery, she heard that the Arts Council had awarded her a grant of £2,500 to give her time to compose more music. It bought one year's child care for her five-month-old baby, allowed her to write *Commedia* and to make the move with her husband to Scotland. *Commedia* is a striking work and met with ecstatic reviews. Beamish's move to Scotland seems to have been an unmitigated success. With her husband, she has founded the Chamber Group of Scotland. She speaks glowingly of the liveliness and energy of a gathering of composers and players. A second child and the lack of a publisher for her music have failed to stop the flow of compositions. She feels no sense of disadvantage as a woman. Instead, she appears positively to relish the discipline of having to compose fast during the few hours a day when the babysitter is present, while praising the limitless patience and support of her husband. Beamish appears serenely happy. Last month alone, ten performances of her work took place.

So what next? Beamish's thirty-two works have been mostly for chamber music groups. A new violin concerto will be premiered next year but her real ambition is to write an opera. No one has commissioned it. Perhaps an offer from the viola thief might be appropriate.

1   What was the effect of the robbery on Sally Beamish?
    A It made her start composing.
    B It made her work harder.
    C It caused her to stop playing viola music.
    D It confirmed a certain course of action.

2   What is unusual about her early childhood?
    A She had difficulties with spelling.
    B She could play the piano at a very young age.
    C She could write music at a very young age.
    D She read a lot of books.

3   Anthony Gilbert told her that
    A the Principal had recommended his classes.
    B her work was good but unfashionable.
    C she should stop composing.
    D she didn't need to attend his classes.

4   What was the problem at the final rehearsal?
    A The performers didn't want to play it.
    B She wanted to make last-minute changes.
    C The work was not professional enough.
    D It had not won a competition.

5   How does Sally Beamish cope with her present
    domestic circumstances?
    A She does not have time to find a publisher.
    B She needs more support from her husband.
    C She gets help from other composers.
    D She doesn't find them a problem.

6   In her career as a composer, what has been Sally
    Beamish's main problem?
    A Lack of confidence in herself.
    B The stress of living in London.
    C Not getting enough commissions for her music.
    D Lack of time to compose.

2 Read the extract below from the text you have just
read and fill in the missing prepositions.

> Her panic was so great that when she came
> (1) .... attend the final rehearsal (2) ....
> *Dances and Nocturnes*, she took (3) ....
> her pen and made an attempt, resisted
> (4) .... the performers, to cut (5) ....
> several bars of music, (6) .... of fear that
> her music would not be regarded (7) ....
> professional. Later, Beamish entered a work
> (8) .... a competition.

3 Complete this summary of the article by putting the
correct preposition in each space.

> With hard work and determination Sally
> Beamish was able to succeed (1) .... her
> career as a composer, even though the odds
> seemed stacked (2) .... her. The theft of
> her prized viola (which was (3) .... loan)
> had a serious effect (4) .... her; indeed it
> set the seal (5) .... her decision to move to
> a new country.
>
> Despite enrolling (6) .... a musical
> composition course, she began to lose
> confidence (7) .... her own ability. After
> being encouraged (8) .... two famous
> composers, she's found herself back on the
> path (9) .... success. She's been able to
> carry (10) .... regardless (11) .... all the
> family pressures around her.
>
> It might have something to do with her
> husband, who is full of enthusiasm (12) ....
> her work and very patient (13) .... her
> whilst being supportive (14) .... the
> unconventional situation.

VOCABULARY

Word formation (CB page 61)

1 Complete each sentence with the correct form of the word in CAPITALS. Use the prefixes and suffixes in the box to help you. Sometimes a spelling change is also required.

in- -ence -al -ness -ive
-ly -ing -ic -ian

1 The child threw herself to the ground .... and began to cry her eyes out. DRAMA

2 The band gave an .... performance of their latest record. ELECTRIFY

3 Most teenagers expect to be trusted with a little .... by their parents. DEPEND

4 Their dancing has a kind of .... intensity. POEM

5 The author was delighted that his latest book received .... acclaim. CRITIC

6 Nancy cannot work in her study unless it's maintained in a state of .... with everything filed in the correct place. ORDER

7 Patrick is studying at college to become a .... MUSIC

8 The .... was an extremely gripping story of the horrors of war. NARRATE

Tip: When you are reading a text in English, choose ten long words (nouns, verbs, adjectives or adverbs) and try to identify the affixes that have been added to form the word.

Phrasal verbs (CB page 62)

2 Complete the following sentences using a verb from the box in the correct form.

fizzle break run grow pour wash hold iron

1 Some of his greatest inventions .... out of earlier ideas he had but didn't always finish.

2 We had a few problems to start with but we managed to .... them out.

3 The factory strike started in a united way, but then .... out after only two days.

4 We were getting along just fine but then suddenly he .... out a stream of abuse.

5 Philippa still .... out hope that one day she will be a rich person.

6 The New Year is a good time to try and .... out of a rut.

7 The second day of the summer fair was completely .... -out by the torrential rain. (*a passive form*)

8 In six month's time Chris's visa will have .... out and he'll have to go back home.

Tip: One possible way of organising your learning of phrasal verbs is to group them by particle. You could find other phrasal verbs formed with different particles, e.g. *on, in, from* or *by*.

3 Complete the sentences below using the phrasal verbs from the box in the correct form.

fall apart set up get over settle down put out

1 Paul has decided to leave his job and .... a small business.

2 After a stormy ferry crossing, Hazel's stomach finally .... when she landed in France.

3 Don't forget to .... the light before you go to bed.

4 Isn't it time you bought a new pair of shoes? Those look as though they're .... !

5 Tom has finally .... the flu that he caught in the winter.

4 Many phrasal verbs have metaphorical as well as literal meanings. Complete these sentences using the phrasal verbs from Exercise 3 with their metaphorical meanings.

1 When Anita heard the news it was a complete shock and she simply ....

2 The police admitted that Jake hadn't really carried out the robbery – he'd been .... by one of the police officers.

3 Don't you think it's time that you two .... and got married?

4 He's a good teacher but he sometimes has problems .... the main ideas to his students.

5 We'd love to stay for the weekend, but we don't want to .... you ....

ENGLISH IN USE

Part 1, Multiple choice cloze (CB page 59)

For questions **1–15**, read the text below and then decide which word, (**A, B, C** or **D**), best fits each space. Put the letter you choose for each question (**A – D**) in the gap. The exercise begins with an example (**0**).

HOW TO WRITE A BLOCKBUSTER

If you have ever finished reading the (**0**) .A. blockbuster and thought that you could have done better, consider (**1**) .... the following techniques.

Before you settle upon your subject (**2**) .... , be canny and examine the current market. If period dramas are (**3**) .... a comeback, for example, consider that genre but with a unique (**4**) .... . Start by looking around you – in newspapers, on TV – for stories and characters. Choose a genre and topic you feel comfortable with. (**5**) .... research will add to the strength and depth of your writing and help you (**6**) .... more confidence. Read (**7**) .... history books, biographies and travelogues to immerse yourself in your chosen period and (**8**) .... .

Once you have formulated your characters, possible storylines and locations, start to sketch out (**9**) .... dialogues and (**10**) .... . Only then should you set (**11**) .... writing the novel.

Once the novel is completed, you must find an agent. Many (**12**) .... publishers will only consider submissions via an (**13**) .... agent and will largely ignore unsolicited books. Again, research is the key. Look for an agent that (**14**) .... your genre and style. Finally, do not forget that the book has to be marketed once it is published, so you, the author, will become one of the novel's Unique Selling Points. It helps if you and the book have a good story (**15**) .... you too.

0	A latest	B modern	C ate	D new
1	A accepting	B making	C adopting	D doing
2	A theme	B matter	C topic	D issue
3	A taking	B doing	C having	D making
4	A turn	B spin	C spiral	D twist
5	A Full	B Thorough	C Complete	D Entire
6	A gain	B win	C become	D grow
7	A linked	B connected	C relevant	D similar
8	A area	B place	C location	D setting
9	A raw	B uneven	C rough	D underdeveloped
10	A scenes	B places	C pictures	D visions
11	A up	B about	C to	D down
12	A central	B winning	C valued	D leading
13	A established	B knowledgeable	C fixed	D credited
14	A serves	B acts	C shows	D represents
15	A beyond	B behind	C above	D below

LANGUAGE STUDY

Confusible structures (CB page 63)

1 Underline the correct structure in the following sentences.

1 It looks *as/like* it's going to rain.
2 During the summer he worked *as/like* a part-time teacher.
3 She is regarded *as/like* the major painter within the movement.
4 Despite spending years in England, he never got used to *eating/eat* the food.
5 I *am used to/used to smoke/smoking* but I gave up last year.
6 He *is supposed/supposed* to be at work.
7 I *am supposed/suppose* you think that's clever?
8 I suppose *winning/to win* the lottery would make me happy, but I'm not sure.

2 Complete the following sentences with *would* when possible or if not, a form of *used to*.

A: Have you ever worked abroad?
B: Yes. Before I moved here I (1) .... live in Athens. I (2) .... teach in a school in Zographou but lived in Kipseli, which was the other side of town. The buses were on strike for a couple of months and every day I (3) .... have to walk from one side of Athens to the other.
A: That must have been tiring.
B: It wasn't all that bad. I (4) .... allow myself plenty of time so that I could stop and have a coffee halfway there. I (5) .... smoke at the time and (6) .... (not) do any exercise, so it probably did me good.

Present participle clauses (CB page 67)

3 Present participle clauses are often used to create a formal style. Decide which of the following sentences have used them inappropriately and rewrite them using a word from the box. Pay attention to your use of tenses!

after so when which

1 Having addressed the conference, the minister left for Brussels.
....
2 Having washed the car, I made myself a cup of tea.
....

3 A: Did you see the film last night?
   B: No. Feeling tired, I decided to go to bed early.
....
4 Having lost several thousand pounds at the casino, the accused proceeded to argue with the manager.
....
5 A: Does everyone like your new suit?
   B: I don't think so. On my entering the room, they all laughed.
....
6 Placing the ring on her finger, he noticed that Samantha's hand was trembling.
....
7 The ignition then lights the flame, causing the boiler's main jets to open.
....
8 The car broke down again, making me really mad!
....

4 Improve this extract from a story by using present participle clauses where indicated (1–5).

(1) Because *the Inspector was bad at consoling people in these situations* he had always tried to avoid such situations. But he needed to find out from Mrs Kent why anyone would want to kill her husband. And to do it in such a spectacular way – there had been enough explosive under that car to bring down a tower block.
(2) *When he met her the following morning, however*, the Inspector realised he needn't have worried. Mrs Kent was surprisingly calm about the whole thing, (3) *which made him feel even more uneasy about this case*. He'd already discovered that Mr Kent had only recently been parking his car in number 36's drive.
(4) *When he learnt that their neighbour had asked him to park there* in order to make the house look occupied, the Inspector realised that perhaps the whole thing had been a dreadful mistake. Perhaps the killer's target hadn't been Mr Kent at all but our mysterious neighbour. Yet there was still the question of Mrs Kent, who (5) *showed no emotion whatsoever throughout the whole interview* and demanded little from the Inspector in the way of counselling skills.

1 ....
2 ....
3 ....
4 ....
5 ....

ENGLISH IN USE

Part 2, Structural cloze (CB page 64)

1 Read this newspaper article about graffiti on the London Undergound and decide what you think. Is it art or vandalism?

2 Read the text more carefully and try to decide which part of speech is missing. Is it a preposition or a verb, for example? Then complete each gap with one word only. The exercise begins with an example (0).

IS IT ART OR VANDALISM?

Just (0) ..a.. few weeks ago, eight graffiti gang members (1) .... convicted of causing £5,000 (2) .... of damage on the London Underground.

(3) .... are more than seventy hard-core graffiti artists thought to be operating in London today. Graffiti artists operate (4) .... many towns. They often work at night, covering walls, trains and railway stations (5) .... brightly painted murals in spray paint or marker pen.

Some people regard graffiti (6) .... a form of vandalism and a menace. London Underground says that rail users find it ugly and offensive. It spends £2 million a year dealing with graffiti and has (7) .... introduced trains with graffiti-resistant paint. 'We don't think it is artistic or creative. As (8) .... as we're concerned, it's vandalism,' says Serena Holley, a spokeswoman for London Underground. 'It creates a sense of anarchy and chaos,' says Richard Mandel, the barrister (9) .... prosecuted the graffiti gang. 'Passengers feel as (10) .... the whole rail system is (11) .... of control.' Graffiti art can also be a dangerous pastime. Some teenagers have died in accidents (12) .... nocturnal graffiti raids.

However, others say that (13) .... its best graffiti is an art form. 'Of course, graffiti is art. There's (14) .... question about that,' says David Grob, director of the Grob gallery in London. Even some of (15) .... who think it is wrong admit that some of the people who do graffiti are talented. 'It's (16) .... that their talent is channelled in the wrong direction,' says Barry Kogan, the barrister who represented one of the gang members.

WRITING

Part 2, Review (CB page 68)

1 Read this writing task.

Read any good books lately?

We all know that reading is a good way to improve our language ability, so let us know your recommendations. E-mail a review to us of around 250 words giving us a brief outline of the story, characters and where it is set and

WE'LL PUBLISH THE BEST OF THEM ON-LINE!

You are browsing on the Internet and you see the following notice on a web site for English-language students.

Write your **review**. (Write approximately 250 words.)

2 Read the mark scheme for the task. This will tell you what the examiner is looking for in an ideal answer.

Content (points covered): the review must include the name and author of the book being written about; must mention the outline of the story, the characters and setting; should state who it is recommended for.

Organisation and cohesion: the review should be divided into clear paragraphs, e.g.
    paragraph 1 – introduction to the book
    paragraphs 2/3/(4) – description of story, characters and setting
    paragraph 5 – conclusion and recommendation.

Range: should use language suited to a book review i.e. describing events in an economical way; colourful adjectives.

Register: semi-formal.

Target reader: would have enough information to decide if he or she wants to read the book.

Accuracy: should not contain major errors that lead to misunderstandings or have a negative effect on the reader.

---

3 Now read the answer on page 43 and do the questions below.

1 Has the writer included all the essential information? Tick off the list in Exercise 2 **Content**.

2 a) Has the writer organised the review appropriately? Use the paragraph organisation in Exercise 2 to help you decide where paragraph 3 could be split into two separate paragraphs.

    b) Is the linking expression *however* used correctly?

3 a) Underline three adjectives that the writer has used to describe the book and its events and put a tick (✓) next to them.

    b) Underline the parts of the sentence in which the recommendation is made that could be used again in any book review.

    c) The review contains several instances where the writer has repeated certain words or phrases instead of using a synonym. Find the following words or phrases in the review and find a suitable replacement:
      novel (line 3)
      storyteller (line 5)
      a home for the elderly (line 7)
      residents (line 9)
      gentle (line 10)
      confide in (line 13)
      secret relationship (line 15)
      ending (line 18)

4 Find the following errors and make the necessary corrections:
    a repetition of a noun instead of using a reference pronoun (*para 1*)
    a mistake in a compound word (*para 2*)
    an extra preposition that isn't needed and a wrong preposition (*para 3*)
    an incorrect form of a word (*para 3*)

4 Now rewrite the answer using the corrections that you have made.

1 The Brimstone Wedding by Barbara Vine

A novel where the main 'action' takes place in a home for the elderly in a quiet English village doesn't sound particularly thrilling. But don't be fooled by the setting. 'The Brimstone Wedding' is a novel about secrets. 2 One of these secrets is horrifying.

The storyteller of the story is Jenny, a young woman in her early thirties, who has never had a career and who is working as a care assistant at Middleton Hall — a home for the elderly. One day a new resident arrives. Jenny realises that Stella is different from all the other residents she looks after. Although seventy-years-old Stella only has a few months to live, she is intelligent, smart, with a calm and gentle manner that attracts Jenny to her. Stella, in turn, sees Jenny as a friend, not just a gentle nurse. Even though they don't know it, each woman is looking for 3 someone to confide in.

Jenny, who is unhappily married, begins to confide in Stella — and the reader — the joys and heartache of her secret relationship with another man. Stella slowly reveals the story of a secret relationship of Stella's that took place some 40 years previously — one which ends up in a truly shocking ending. Barbara Vine is better known as Ruth Rendell, the 'queen in crime fiction'. However, this is recommended less to those who enjoy a good detective story and more for people interested in the psychologism of human behaviour, particularly the things we do for love.

Commitments

READING
Part 2, Gapped text

1 You are going to read a magazine article about a relationship between a father and his son. Seven paragraphs have been removed. You must choose which of the paragraphs A–H on page 45 match the numbered gaps 1–7. There is one extra paragraph which does not fit in any of the gaps. Use the clues in each gap to help you.

LIKE FATHER, LIKE SON

Like many of his generation, my father was generally reticent at the dinner table. When it came to my friends or the latest fad that gripped my age group, my father seemed to have nothing to say. Or maybe he did, but I wasn't listening. Yet one thing was certain about me and my father, as it is with most fathers and sons. We could talk about sport.

(The first paragraph mentions the close bond the writer has with his father about sport. The next paragraph will probably explain how this bond manifested itself.)

1

As fans we would go to Syracuse University football games dressed in gaudy orange and blue, things I could never have imagined wearing to school. Then under the crisp, grey autumn skies of central New York, my father and I would sit together, alone in a crowd of forty thousand. In unison, we would jump to our feet to cheer a touchdown, or moan when one of our team was sent off.

(The paragraph above describes being at a match. What paragraph continues with this account?)

2

As I grew, my own life's focus shifted from that of sports fan to athlete. Adolescence, a time for cars and girls, is the most difficult test for the bonds between different generations. Once again, sport was the arbitrator. Of course, my father was never allowed to give advice, but I could ask for it. How did I play in today's game? What wrestling moves did he think were best? Did I have a chance of winning the state title?

(The preceding paragraph lists a number of questions. Which paragraph makes reference to answering these questions?)

3

My father was always there, winning or losing as I won or lost. My broken bones and torn ligaments seemed to hurt him more than me. Success would lift me for days while it carried him for weeks. Sometimes there were wrestling tournaments in distant towns. My parents were the ones who got some cheap roadside motel room and spent the entire weekend watching me, my own personal fan club. Whatever I did, my father always supported me.

(Which paragraph gives examples of the way the writer's father supported him?)

4

Remarkably, his outward expectations of me were low. When, as a child, I announced that one day I would win a state wrestling title and get a college football scholarship, he nodded and said, 'That would be nice.' Later he would tell me that this was so I wouldn't think he expected too much.

(The paragraph after the gap refers to the writer's wife and Thane. Which paragraph tells you who Thane is?)

5

After the Falcons, the team I play for now, have won a match, my wife lowers Thane over the railing that separates the fans from the players. I carry him out onto the field to show him off to my team-mates. He runs his tiny fingers through my sweat-matted hair and explains, 'Mummy will wait for us outside because only the guys can go into the locker room.' I nod and laugh, setting him down so he can chase me across the turf and

into the tunnel. 'That's right,' I tell him. 'Only the guys. Just you and me son.'

(The paragraph above tells us of the relationship between the writer and his own son. Which paragraph continues this theme?)

6

I plan to throw and catch a lot of whatever kind of ball my son decides to pick up over the next fifteen years. I plan to eat a lot of hot-dogs at the nearest college stadium. I plan to hurry out of countless important meetings, grinning foolishly and explaining that I have to get to the high school in time for the first whistle of the football game.

(The following paragraph tells us that the writer expects his son to be interested in a number of different sports. Which paragraph introduces this idea?)

7

Of course, I can imagine him as a professional footballer like me. But because of my own father, I am wise enough to know that the kind of sport doesn't matter. What matters is that there is a sport, something we can watch and talk about and worry about ... together.

A Everything was always OK with my father. Tears of frustration caused by failure were OK. I could quit if I really wanted to. Tears of joy were OK too, when I was picked to play for a professional team.

B I realise that since he is only three, his remembrance of all this may be cloudy at best. But it is the beginning of the bond that holds me to my own father. It is a bond I will be sure to nurture and cultivate.

C Sport was a magical medium through which we could see each other clearly. We could be friends. We could talk. We could support the same team. We could even wear the same clothes in our team colours.

D And now I have a son of my own. Thane is only three, but already he is making my life in sports more memorable. I still ask my own father after a game how he thinks I played and I still talk to him about skills and techniques. But now, when I do something good in a game, I raise my arms high and search for my own son's face in the roaring crowd.

E On each occasion, I was aware of how useful these lessons had been and I determined that they would be what I would try and make my own son realise when the time came. Whatever the differences in the opportunities we might have, I had a model for how the relationship should develop.

F Hidden in my father's answers to my questions about sport were the secrets to life: work hard, be honest with yourself and others, never give up. In the context of sports, I devoured these lessons. If he had tried to teach me with stern lectures, it would never have worked.

G Because of the wealth that professional football has provided me with, allowing Thane to grow up in an atmosphere of tennis courts and golf courses, he may become interested in different sports from the baseball, football and hockey that I played as a kid.

H We might have been two steel workers having lunch high up on a beam. Everything around us, even the mayhem of the muddy contest on the pitch below us, seemed small and remote. It was us that counted and what each of us had to say or think about the game. The rest of the world was far away.

Strategy

1 Read the main text first. Even though it has missing parts, you should still be able to get a general understanding.

2 Quickly read the missing paragraphs.

3 Focus on each gap in turn and read the information around the gap, as this is where the links are.

4 Look out for pronouns, linking words and synonyms that may help you.

5 When you have finished, read the whole text through to see if your answers make sense.

2 Find a word or phrase from the text that fits in the sentences below.

Paragraph 1 (Beginning *Like many of his generation*)

1 Does your sister still want a yo-yo for her birthday or is it just a passing .... ?

2 I can't tell you if he intends to stay with the company or not. He's being rather .... about his plans at the moment.

Paragraph 2 (Beginning *As fans we would*)

3 The shops have acted .... with the police to find ways of reducing shoplifting. (2 words)

4 They're missing their star player. He was .... by the referee for deliberately kicking another player. (phrasal verb)

5 His mum has knitted him a really dreadful cardigan. The colours are so ....

Paragraph 4 (Beginning *My father was always*)

6 Unfortunately she lost the race because of a torn .... in her leg.

Paragraph 6 (Beginning *After the Falcons*)

7 Have you seen him .... that expensive new sports car of his? (phrasal verb)

8 They should never have held that Horse of the Year show at the stadium. The .... is totally ruined.

VOCABULARY

Prepositions (CB pages 82/83)

1 Look at pages 82/83 of the Coursebook and complete this summary of Amanda's experience by filling in the correct preposition.

A dream that turned (1) .... a nightmare. I suppose that's what I'd describe my year out in America (2) .... Perhaps it was silly of me to commit myself (3) .... an *au pair's* job when my experience working (4) .... children was limited (5) .... the odd evening baby-sitting and a bit of voluntary work. When I first got there it all made a big impression (6) .... me – the house, the swimming pool, the fact that the couple had good jobs (7) .... the medical profession. Although I had certain duties written (8) .... my contract, my employees were just exploiting me. It took a while for me to admit this; in fact, I took the blame (9) .... myself before having the courage to voice my fears (10) .... the agency. I'd advise anyone in a similar situation to get out quickly.

Phrasal verbs

2 Look at the list of definitions (1–9) and match each one with a phrasal verb (A–I) that is similar in meaning.

1	manage something	A	stick to
2	end a relationship with somebody	B	split up
3	deceive somebody	C	let down
4	trust somebody to do something	D	depend on
5	meet with somebody	E	cheat on
6	persevere with something	F	pile up
7	disappoint somebody	G	get together
8	maintain something	H	hold down
9	increase	I	keep up

3 Complete these dialogues with one of the phrasal verbs above in the correct form.

1 A: I can't remember the last time we went out.
   B: Let's .... next week and have a coffee.

2 A: Have you heard that Mary's husband has been .... her with another woman?
   B: Really? I thought Philip was the type of person you could .... Do you think they're going to .... ?

3 A: Are you finding it easy to ....
   .... your new job after that promotion?
   B: I must admit that the work ....
   .... if I don't stay late at least twice a week.

4 A: Have you put on some weight?
   B: I'm afraid so. I'm finding it very hard to
   .... this diet.

5 A: What did you think of my sales presentation yesterday? I'm afraid the one before was pretty poor.
   B: I'm glad you haven't .... me
   .... this time. .... the good work!

Collocation

4 The words in *italics* in the following sentences all form part of common collocations. Complete them with the correct noun from the box. In each box there is one word you do not need.

> duty   care   obligation   requirement
>   commitment   responsibility

1 Don't feel *under any* .... to take on this job if you really dislike the idea.
2 In many countries, crash helmets are *a legal* .... for motorcycling.
3 By passing the new law, the government has *done its* .... to protect the weak.
4 Sandra has made *a firm* .... to meet you next week.
5 The children need to *take* .... for their actions.

> vow   oath   word   guarantee   pledge   promise

6 After being caught stealing from the office Stella *gave her* .... that she wouldn't do it again.
7 The president was questioned *under* ....
   about actions he had undertaken while in power.
8 You can bring the video player back to the shop for a refund providing it is still *under* ....
9 Despite the problems in the company, Jack has received *a/an* .... of support from his colleagues.
10 Don't you remember *making a/an* .... to love me in sickness and in health?

ENGLISH IN USE
Part 4, Word formation

1 Complete these sentences with the correct form of the word in CAPITALS. Use your dictionary if necessary.

1 You'll need to have a lot more piano .... if you want to make a career in music. PRACTISE

2 It's a very unfortunate .... to be in. SITUATE

3 After hearing the distressing news Louise was given some .... by the doctor. SEDATE

4 I hope we can find a suitable .... for the head of department. REPLACE

5 That ship has made a number of .... of the Channel. CROSS

6 The most important quality an army officer needs is .... LEAD

7 You'd make a good novelist as you're such an .... person. IMAGINE

8 There will need to be substantial .... in our expenses if the company is to survive. REDUCE

9 He is a hardened criminal who has earned a considerable .... NOTORIOUS

10 Successful artists need both skill and .... CREATE

2 Complete these sentences with the correct form of the word in CAPITALS. Choose from the following suffixes and negative prefixes, where necessary.

| Suffixes: -ed -ful -ic -able -ly |
| Prefixes: dis- il- in- im- ir- |

1 The car Fran drives is a maroon-.................. BMW. COLOUR

2 Your younger brother is a most .... child. DELIGHT

3 I find Gerald .... difficult to work with. POSSIBLE

4 What a pity that so many children are poor and .... in today's society. ADVANTAGE

5 It won't be confirmed until next week but I can tell you .... that you've got the job. OFFICIAL

6 I can't tolerate this .... behaviour. ACCEPT

7 You'll never get a vase like that one you've just broken! It's .... REPLACE

8 You'll have to write more clearly than this. Your handwriting is almost .... LEGIBLE

9 What a beautiful painting. I had no idea you were so .... ARTIST

10 We regret that tonight's concert has been cancelled and postponed .... DEFINITE

3 Use the words in the box to form one word that fits in the numbered space in the text. The exercise begins with an example (0).

GETTING THE RIGHT BALANCE
Martin Brown was one of the most **(0)** .....successful..... salesman his company had ever employed. He was soon offered **(1)** .... , as the company's sales **(2)** .... in Australia. This would mean a higher salary and more **(3)** .... but also a one-year separation from his family. Since he was already feeling a lot of **(4)** .... about the lack of time he spent with his family, he was rather **(5)** .... about such a long absence. He asked several friends for **(6)** .... and made a decision to ask the company to change the terms of his new **(7)** .... so that his family could accompany him to Australia. Fortunately, the company agreed to this despite the additional expense that would be involved.

(0)	**SUCCESS**	(4)	ANXIOUS
(1)	PROMOTE	(5)	ENTHUSE
(2)	REPRESENT	(6)	ADVISE
(3)	RESPONSIBLE	(7)	APPOINT

A HOTEL FOR ALL THE FAMILY
The Winchester Hotel Group offers an entirely new concept in hotel accommodation. In our new hotels, all in modern **(8)** .... and attractive **(9)** .... close to road and rail links, we provide an environment which is ideal for parents with small children or elderly **(10)** .... . Instead of providing the facilities that business **(11)** .... expect, we have created safe, comfortable hotels which are perfect for families. There are also facilities for the **(12)** .... in all our hotels. (**(13)** ...., pets are not permitted – this is because of our **(14)** .... to cleanliness and **(15)** .... .) For a free brochure, phone 223812.

(8)	BUILD	(12)	ABLE
(9)	LOCATE	(13)	FORTUNE
(10)	RELATE	(14)	COMMIT
(11)	TRAVEL	(15)	SAFE

LANGUAGE STUDY

Making suggestions, recommendations, giving warnings (CB pages 85/86)

1 Most, but not all, of the statements below contain mistakes. Correct those that you find.

1 The police are warning drivers drive carefully due to the freezing conditions. They are suggesting to stay at home unless absolutely necessary.

2 Ah Clara. I've recommended that you are moved to a higher level. I suggest you to speak to your new teacher about any work she has covered.

3 The Government inspectors are advising not to eat meat without washing it first. They also warn cooking chicken thoroughly before eating it.

4 We recommend you that you don't surf the Internet at busy periods. We suggest you try when it is still early in America.

2 <u>Underline</u> the correct word in these sentences. What does *it* refer to in each sentence?

1 If I can make a *suggestion/recommendation*, why don't you try servicing the car more often? Then it wouldn't keep breaking down.

2 This is your last *warning/advice*. If you don't hand your work in on time, I won't be able to mark it.

3 According to the latest medical *recommendations/ suggestions*, people shouldn't cut down smoking but simply give it up.

4 If you want my *advice/suggestion*, I'd save your letter to floppy disk so you have a second copy of it.

3 Rewrite each sentence in Exercise 2 using appropriate patterns from this table.

suggest	doing something
warn	someone (not) to do something
recommend	that someone do something
advise	someone to do something

1 He suggested ....
2 She warned ....
3 The Government has recommended ....
    ....
4 She advised ....

4 Rewrite each of the statements below using the words given.

1 He didn't get picked for the team but he wasn't disappointed.
    In spite of ....

2 I'm not working late tonight. I don't care how much he begs me.
    No matter ....

3 The team have been playing well, even though they have been hit by a lot of injuries.
    Despite ....

4 I know you got 80 per cent for your last test, but you still need to do some practice.
    You may ....

5 It doesn't matter how much I study phrasal verbs, I can't understand them.
    However ....

6 I told him to arrive 30 minutes before the test but he was still late.
    In spite of ....

7 He can apologise but I'm still not speaking to him.
    Even ....

8 He saw a few things he liked but he didn't buy anything.
    Even ....

ENGLISH IN USE

Part 6, Discourse cloze

1 Complete the following sentences (1–6) with the correct ending (A–F).

1 Although I've been learning English a long time,   ..E.
2 I've been studying phrasal verbs for years;   ....
3 We haven't been getting on recently, and   ....
4 I'm thinking of having a holiday abroad this year, ...
5 He's very quiet when he first meets people, ...
6 He's always chatting to his neighbours, and   ....

A they hear all about his personal problems.
B somewhere I can be sure of decent weather.
C hardly a day passes without an argument.
D but he livens up quite soon.
E I just can't seem to make any progress with it.
F however, I still don't understand them.

2 Refer to the discourse cloze exercise in Unit 3 page 25. Which of the points made in the **Strategy** box helped you join the sentences together?

3 Read the following text and then choose from the list
(**A–J**) the phrase which best fits each space (**1–6**). Some
of the suggested answers do not fit at all. The exercise
begins with an example (**0**).

If you would like some help with this exercise, look at
Exercise 4 first.

JAMES' STORY

In my opinion, our marriage works because we
do things together. We are also quite similar –
(**0**) ..J. although I'm possibly a bit quieter than
Beryl, my wife. We both agree that it is important
that we are tolerant of each other,

(**1**) .... because she is so particular about
cleanliness. It's not that I am untidy or messy,
particularly, but I might say something like,
'You're too fussy', although that is as far as it will
go. We don't have rows about it. I also try to
listen to my wife's point of view (**2**) .... . Many
couples break up nowadays because they get too
much money too easily. When we were first
married, money was tight. I earned half as much
on the farm as when I was in the army.

I am not a romantic man, (**3**) .... , although
occasionally I have bought my wife flowers or
chocolates. I even give her a card on our wedding
anniversary, although I have to put it in my diary
so I don't forget. On our tenth I bought her a food
processor, (**4**) .... although we did go to Bermuda
on our twenty- fifth. We'll probably go back for
our golden wedding. (**5**) .... , especially at our
age, although we try to show appreciation. For
example, we say thank you if someone has done
something for the other. (**6**) .... , we're the same
sort of people that we were when we first met.
Maybe that's why it worked.

A	even though I usually buy her a lot of presents
B	I suppose we take each other for granted
C	so that can't be the key to a long marriage
D	but I can't remember what we did on our last one
E	although I was working much harder
F	I don't think our marriage has changed
G	although that doesn't mean I agree with her.
H	despite the fact that we both enjoy playing golf
I	although I sometimes get a bit irritated
J	neither of us is particularly extrovert

4 Underline the following clues in the text and the
phrases that can help you decide which phrase fits
each space.

Example: Gap **0**
The pronoun 'we' before gap (**0**) refers to the same
people as the pronoun 'us' in sentence **J**, and the word
'quieter' in the sentence is the opposite of the word
'extrovert' in **J**. These are good clues that this is the
correct answer.
Gap 1   link word/antonym
Gap 2   link word/different expression
Gap 3   link word/pronoun
Gap 4   link word/pronoun
Gap 5   antonym/link word
Gap 6   statement – an example

WRITING
Part 2, Report (CB page 80)

1 Read this writing task.

> An international magazine is carrying out some research into young people's attitudes in different parts of the world towards elderly people. Give an outline of the situation in your country and state whether the situation is likely to change in the future. Write your **report**. (Write approximately 250 words.)

obrys

2 Read the mark scheme for the task. This will tell you what the examiner is looking for in an ideal answer.

> **Content (points covered):** the report must state clearly which country is being written about; must explain young people's attitudes towards the elderly and possibly give reasons for their attitudes; must explain likely changes and may give recommendations.
>
> **Organisation and cohesion:** the report should be divided into clear paragraphs, e.g.
>
> > paragraph 1 – introduction
> > paragraphs 2/3 – description and explanation of attitudes
> > paragraph 4 – likely changes/conclusion (summary or recommendation).
>
> **Range:** should use language suited to a report e.g. describing trends and making comparisons (*There has been an increase in …/Compared with ten years ago…*).
>
> **Register:** formal. The tone of the report should be fairly neutral and only give a personal view in the conclusion.
>
> **Target reader:** would be informed about the situation in that particular country.
>
> **Accuracy:** should not contain major errors that lead to misunderstandings or have a negative effect on the reader.

provázanost

3 Now read the answer on page 51 and do the questions below.

1. a) Look back at the list of points that should be covered in Exercise 2 **Content**. Put a tick (✓) against the ones the writer has dealt with.
    b) Is there any information in the report that is not relevant to the answer? If so, cross it out.
    c) Are there any points that could be expanded? Use the (⅄) symbol to mark where more information could be given.

2. Has the writer organised the report appropriately? Use the paragraph organisation in Exercise 2 to help you divide paragraph 3 into two separate paragraphs.

3. Find and highlight three useful phrases in the first paragraph that could be used in any report. Put a (✓) next to them.

4. Find the following errors and make the necessary corrections:
    incorrect use of definite article (*para 1*)
    incorrect use of a present tense (*para 2*)
    incorrect preposition (*para 2*)
    two occasions where a gerund form should be used (*para 2*)
    incorrect use of a contracted form (*para 3*)

4 Now write an answer of your own.

Caring for the elderly

1 The aim of this report is to describe the attitudes of the young people towards elderly folk. Although I was born in France I have lived in Ireland for the last seven years so I will write my report on Ireland. This important topic raises a number of interesting questions such as

– What do the youth think about old people?

– What do old people think about the young?

   This report will try to answer these questions.

2 Compared to France it seems that young people in Ireland are quite interested in old people. On the bus, for example, you can see a young boy or teenager standing up when an elderly person is getting on, so that person can sit down with comfort. In the secondary school I go to there is a scheme called 'Community Help' Every month two of the pupils go to visit an old person to do jobs for them, things like shopping or tidy the garden, or even just sitting and having a chat. This stops the old people to get lonely.

3 Some young people, however, say that it is boring to be with the elderly, or that old people do not respect them. Sometimes when young people play outside in the street an old woman may call the police even though there is no crime. To finish this report I would say that I dont think the situation will change in the future. I hope that the young people will continue to care for the elderly in a kind way. Both young and old must tolerate each other.

Home sweet home

READING

Part 3, Multiple choice

1 Read the following article from a newspaper about two couples who have farms in Spain. Answer the multiple choice questions on page 53 by circling the best answer, **A**, **B**, **C** or **D**.

It's no Eldorado, but the tough, self-sufficient life of rural Spain

Goodbye to suburbia

IF YOU met Les and Jo or Kevin and Tania in England, you would not be surprised to learn that Les was a mechanic, Jo worked for social services, Kevin in a steel works and Tania in an electronics factory. That is what they did several years ago before they moved to Spain to work the land.

Six years ago, Les and Jo moved to the Alpujarras, a mountainous region between Granada and the Costa del Sol. Rural depopulation had enabled Les and Jo to buy land fairly cheaply. The nearest village, Castaras, sits on a rocky promontory one thousand metres above sea-level, on the flank of the Sierra Nevada mountain range. Les and Jo's farm is in a green and fertile valley far below the village. You have to splash through a stream to get to their tiny farm. It is a ten-minute walk from the end of a steep dirt track. Les and Jo come from Yorkshire and until recently were the only foreigners living permanently in the valley.

Their life is hard. For Jo, taking her cheese to market means rising before dawn to saddle the mule to carry the produce. Kevin takes the olives to the mill in a wheelbarrow. Sitting outside a bar on market day, Les, who is forty, explains his belief in a natural cycle of agriculture. He breaks off to talk in the local dialect to a man to whom he sold a calf. But even among organic farmers, there can be few who

rely so totally on man and animal power. Les's method of threshing grain, using a mule on a stone platform, is centuries old. The irrigation system, built hundreds of years ago, which made this one of the most productive areas of Southern Spain, is virtually unaltered and the mule remains dominant on the small, steeply-terraced fields. The ancient olive trees must still be picked by hand, using canes to knock the fruit onto nets. This is the way that Les, who used to work as a mechanic on farms in North Yorkshire, prefers to farm.

Les and Jo moved from their first smallholding two years ago to get more land and a house. They say they don't need a large income. They say they grow most

---

'I wanted to have my own land and there was no way I could do that in England'

---

of their own food. They sell their cheese, made from the milk of one cow. They grow almonds, which go into their own confectionery bars. The recipe came from a vegetarian cookery book but the bars are sold – six hundred a week in the summer – as a typical local product in the tourist villages. Jo and Les accept their low income because they love the life, but they understand why local young people will not follow the way of life of their parents.

'Being seen to work hard is very important if you are to be accepted into a country community anywhere. When we came, we hardly noticed, we were so busy, but after a couple of years we found we were being introduced as "the foreigners who work hard". Sometimes we differ from the local people. For example, over our refusal to use chemical fertilisers and pesticides. That is accepted.' They spend long hours listening to the old people. 'I think they are glad they can pass on their knowledge to us,' said Les. Jo, who before coming here, worked in an old people's home, added 'We both enjoy talking to elderly people.' Les admits, 'We owe everything we know about farming here to the Spanish people. I don't look at it as two communities.'

Some miles away, Kevin and Tania are picking lemons, milking goats, collecting eggs and carrying hay. Five years ago, they lived in Hampshire, a typical young couple on a modern estate with a mortgage and a car. 'Don't make the Alpujarras sound like

paradise,' said Tania. 'It's not. It's hard work, but we are working for ourselves. In England, we were just working to pay the mortgage and run my car and Kevin's motor bike so that we could get to work to earn the money to pay the mortgage,' said Tania. Kevin had worked as a gardener and on a farm but ended up in a steel works because the wages were double what he could earn on the land. Tania had worked with horses and then as a florist but eventually took a job in an electronics factory. 'Why is it that the jobs you enjoy doing don't pay? When I left the factory, they told me I was making a mistake. I was giving up a promising career. They could not understand what we were doing,' she said. They had decided that they wanted to have some land. 'We came here on holiday and decided it was the place to be.' Kevin recently made his first visit to England since settling in Spain and is more certain than ever that he does not want to return. 'It would mean working for somebody else.'

1 Before moving to Spain, the four people in the article
   A had ordinary jobs.
   B earned a lot of money.
   C worked in agriculture.
   D developed the skills they needed.

2 Les and Jo bought their land in an area where
   A other foreigners had already settled.
   B many local people had left.
   C they can see the sea.
   D the land is flat.

3 Les's method of working
   A is the same as most local farmers.
   B is one he strongly believes in.
   C was imposed on him by his lack of machinery.
   D was learned on farms in England.

4 What do Les and Jo think of tourists?
   A They are a market for their products.
   B They are a source of great profit.
   C They are people who are easily deceived.
   D They are responsive to new products.

5 Local people think Les and Jo are
   A temporary residents.
   B old-fashioned.
   C making a great effort.
   D taking advantage of local knowledge.

6 When Kevin and Tania lived in England they felt
   A the work they did was productive.
   B they would have to reduce their expenses.
   C they were in jobs with good prospects.
   D what mattered was how much they earned.

7 What is the continued attraction of living in Spain for Kevin and Tania?
   A They enjoy the hard work.
   B They love the simple life.
   C They want to be independent.
   D They like eating their own fresh food.

2 Match one word from Column A with one from Column B to form word combinations which appeared in the text on page 52.

A	B	
social	fertilisers	1 ....
low	bars	2 ....
virtually	career	3 ....
confectionery	dialect	4 ....
local	unaltered	5 ....
chemical	income	6 ....
promising	services	7 ....

3 Use appropriate word combinations from Exercise 2 to complete the following sentences.

1 It's all very well learning the standard form of a language but it doesn't help much when you go to the villages and hear the .... being spoken.

2 Booth's is a traditional company which produces cakes, biscuits and different types of ....

3 Families who live on a .... are usually entitled to financial help from the state.

4 Many customers are becoming increasingly worried about the amount of .... that are sprayed on our fruit and vegetables.

5 Amanda has given up a .... in the legal profession in order to do voluntary work overseas.

6 My grandparents' house has remained .... since the day they moved in some twenty years ago.

VOCABULARY

Prepositions

1 Complete the sentences with the correct preposition. Try to learn the completed expressions.

1 You shouldn't make your mind up until you've heard the *background* .... the story.
2 .... *view* .... this serious matter, you are advised to seek a solicitor.
3 It doesn't seem fair that Holly's boss will only let her go on that training course .... her *own expense*.
4 The cottage is beautifully furnished and .... *close proximity* to the beach.
5 Chris isn't involved in the *day*-..........-*day* running of the business.
6 .... *the face* .... all the criticism from his colleagues, the Managing Director decided to resign.
7 We need to *keep an eye* .... the timetable to make sure that production doesn't slide.
8 The employees on strike *despised the others* .... carrying on with their work.
9 Asthma is an illness *characterised* .... breathing problems and a tight chest.
10 The need to work harder to prevent job cuts was *impressed* .... the firm by the management.

Around the home (CB page 91)

2 Look at the following three words and, using a dictionary if necessary, find as many different forms of each word as possible.

> proud   home   clean

3 Now use one of the forms you found in Exercise 2 to complete the sentences below.

proud

1 Michael .... himself on keeping an immaculate home.
2 Deborah is always cleaning and tidying up. I wish I could be as ....-.................. as she is. (compound adjective)
3 I can't wait to move in to my new flat – it's my .... and joy.

home

4 Painting your living room in that warm colour was a good idea. It looks much more ...homely... and welcoming than it used to.

5 When Craig lost his job and couldn't pay the rent, he found himself .... for a short spell.
6 Are these tomatoes ....-.................. or did you buy them from the supermarket. (*compound adjective*)
7 The first time I lived abroad, I was really .... for my family and friends.
8 It only took us two hours to get to our holiday cottage so I'm hoping the .... journey will be just as trouble-free.

clean

9 If the housework gets too much for you, you could always employ a .... to do it.
10 I've decided to give my house a thorough ....-.................. this weekend starting with the backs of my cupboards. (*compound noun*)
11 The inspectors complimented the staff at the restaurant on the .... of their kitchen.
12 Make sure you .... that cut properly before you put a plaster on it. You may get an infection in it otherwise.

ENGLISH IN USE

Part 5, Register cloze (CB pages 98/99)

1 Using a dictionary if necessary, match the following informal expressions (1–8) with their more formal equivalents (A–H).

1 to put up with ....
2 to look into ....
3 to do away with ....
4 to fall out with ....
5 to see eye to eye ....
6 to be given the sack ....
7 to hold your tongue ....
8 to come up to scratch ....

A to have a disagreement with someone
B to reach expectations
C to be dismissed from your job
D to remain silent
E to investigate
F to tolerate
G to abolish
H to be in agreement

2 Complete the following sentences with the most appropriate expression from Exercise 1. You will need to change the form of the verb.

1 I haven't been .... with Sam recently. We always seem to be arguing about the most trivial matters.

2 He was caught stealing from the company and ....

3 We've been .... the idea of building our own home.

4 Have you heard? Frank .... his girlfriend again. This time she's called the wedding off.

5 They're thinking of .... state pensions and replacing them with private ones.

6 Our teacher's so strict! He won't .... any playing around at all.

7 His company have decided he .... and so they're not going to renew his contract.

8 What a noise! Will you .... just for a moment while I'm on the phone!

3 Read the note from a surveyor about a house. Use the information in it to complete the numbered spaces in the formal letter to an estate agent. The words you need do not occur in the informal note. Use no more than two words for each gap. The exercise begins with an example (0).

Strategy

1 Read both texts through first.
2 Underline or highlight the words and phrases in the first text that you have to rewrite for the second text.
3 Ensure that the information you have added to the second text is the same and that the grammar is also correct.

INFORMAL NOTE

Dear Tom and Maria,

Just a quick note to let you know that I had a good look round the house in Marchant Street for you. To get straight to the point, if you buy it you will have to do it up — definitely. And it will cost you a lot. There are so many things that need fixing that I just gave up listing them — but all of them really must be done. For example, there is no central heating and four windows have been completely smashed — nothing there at all. Anyone could get in at the moment, although there is nothing inside worth stealing. When it comes to the garden, well, it's a jungle. I thought you said there was a gardener? If so, he hasn't put himself out. No one has done a thing to the house or garden for ages. If I were you, I'd think again about the offer you made. Cut it, if you still want the house. No fee of course — a favour to my good friends!
Best wishes
Tim

LETTER TO ESTATE AGENT

Dear Mr Grabbit

Our surveyor **(0)** ...has informed.... us that he has made a **(1)** ...... of 27 Marchant Street on our **(2)** ..... . It appears that the property needs **(3)** ..... and that this will be very **(4)** .... . Our surveyor **(5)** ..... his attempt to make a comprehensive list of the work that is absolutely **(6)** ..... . However, he noted the **(7)** ..... central heating and that four windows are completely **(8)** ..... . Currently, the property is not secure, although it contains nothing **(9)** ..... . As for the garden, it has not been properly looked after for a long time. **(10)** ..... the information you gave us, a gardener had been employed. If this is the case, he seems to have made **(11)** ..... . In fact both the house and garden seem to have been neglected for quite some time. While we are still interested in purchasing this house, we have been obliged **(12)** ..... , and now feel that we must make a **(13)** ..... offer of £250,000.

Yours sincerely

Tom and Maria Jenkins

LANGUAGE STUDY

Talking about the future (CB page 96)

1 Two of the three options in the following texts are correct. <u>Underline</u> them.

1 Yes, I think they've organised everything for the wedding now. Her parents *arrive/are arriving/will arrive* on Saturday, Teresa *will phone/is going to phone/is phoning* us back to let us know if Craig will be the best man and Harry *will be taking/is going to take/takes* the photos. Just think, this time next month they *will be sitting/are going to be sitting/will sit* on the beach in Barbados on their honeymoon.

2 We're not doing too badly. We've decorated most of the upstairs. I think we *will have to/are going to have to/have to* call in a plumber next week though to finish off the kitchen. We've already started stripping the walls in the living room so I think by the weekend we *will have finished/finish/will finish* that room. Then a week on Saturday Tom and Sheila *are coming/will come/will be coming* round for the housewarming party.

3 Well, we *will buy/are going to buy/are buying* a charter rather than a scheduled ticket. It's so much cheaper. I *am going to book/am booking/will book* non-smoking seats. I don't care what Maria says. It seems that we *are going to be/will be/will have been* able to check in quite late if we don't have much baggage.

2 Make the following statements less formal by using an appropriate future tense. You should use a different tense in each case.

1 I've made arrangements to see the doctor at 3.00.
2 We intend to move into a bigger house next year.
3 The course is scheduled to start on May 13th.
4 The roadworks are expected to be complete before the busy summer period.
5 Please, allow me to do that for you.
6 Judging by the feeling in my stomach, I am about to be sick.
7 I will be in the process of meeting the Director at that time.
8 I think there is a possibility of them winning, as long as the crowd get behind them.

Future time in subordinate clauses (CB page 97)

3 Combine the following pairs of sentences using the word given.

1 Let him have dinner. Then I'll tell him the bad news.
Once ....
2 We're going to Paris. We'll be staying with relations.
When ....
3 I'm doing the exam in June. I think I'll be good enough to pass by then.
.... by the time ....
4 I'll be getting paid on Friday. I won't be able to lend you any money until then.
.... until ....
5 I'll finish working on the car first. Then I'll take you into town.
As soon as ....
6 I'm going shopping. Will you wait for the phone call?
.... while .... ?
7 Will you be able to show proof of purchase? If so, we will change the goods.
Provided ....
8 The Government might be raising interest rates. Small businesses are going to be in trouble.
If ....

4 Complete the following letter using an appropriate future form of the verbs in brackets.

... anyway, everything's organised and we
(1) .... (arrive) on the 19th. When we
(2) .... (get) to the airport I
(3) .... (give) you a ring. I've arranged to spend a few days with a friend in London. I
(4) .... (stay) at her place for the first weekend. I (5) .... (be) busy during the first few days. But hopefully, by the time I
(6) .... (meet) you on 25th I
(7) .... (complete) all my business commitments and we (8) .... (able to) spend some time together. I've an idea! I.
(9) .... (call) Frances and see if she'd like to meet with us as well. As soon as I
(10) .... (write) this I
(11) .... (phone) her and arrange it. So, I (12) .... (look) forward to seeing you! I
(13) .... (finish) now and get on with my packing. Just think, this time in a few weeks we
(14) .... (laugh) around your dinner table just like old times!

ENGLISH IN USE

Part 3, Error correction (CB pages 55/93)

1 As you saw in Unit 4, there are often mistakes in the following areas of punctuation in the error correction task. Find an example of each mistake in the sentences opposite and correct it.

- capitals
- full stops
- commas in relative clauses
- apostrophes (in contractions and possessives)
- punctuation in direct speech
- natural pauses in sentences
- lists
- hyphens in compounds

1 The Prime Minister who is visiting the middle east, warned against strike action.
2 Look at that bird. I think it's wing is injured.
3 They've got a three year old daughter.
4 Have you got any plans for new year's eve?
5 Can you get me some sugar a tin of soup and a loaf of bread?
6 'We have every officer available working on the case, the chief constable said.
7 Always look carefully for punctuation errors in sentences
8 Actually I think we had better be leaving now.

2 In most of the lines in the following text, there is either a spelling or a punctuation error. For each numbered line, write the correctly spelled word or show the correct punctuation. Some lines are correct. Indicate these lines with a tick (✓). The exercise begins with three examples (**0**).

A REAL HOUSE-WARMING PARTY

0	*charades, in*	A Christmas night game of charades in which people mime
0	*well-known*	the titles of wellknown films and books, was in full swing
0	*Inferno*	when Nicholas Gaunt started miming The Towering Infernoe
1	....	for his guests. He acted out the 1970s disaster film in which
2	....	an office block is engulfed in flames. It was at a crucial
3	....	moment in his performance that he noticed a wooden beam
4	....	above the fire turning black. I put my hand on it and it was
5	....	very hot. I realised the beam was actually smouldering
6	....	and said we should call the Fire Brigade imediately,' Mr
7	....	Gaunt 52, said. Fire crews reached the house within five
8	....	minutes as family and freinds cleared the room of furniture
9	....	as it began to fill with smoke. Mr Gaunt said that he planned
10	....	to point to the fire as a clue in the game of charades. 'I dont
11	....	know why I thought of that film,' said Mr Gaunt, 'but it
12	....	turned out to be really apropriate, and very lucky'. Firemen said
13	....	the beam had been smouldering for quite a long time and
14	....	was about to burst into flames. They supported the cieling and
15	....	removed the beam and part of the stone fireplace. Mr Gaunts
16	....	daugter, Rebecca, said it had been a very dramatic evening.

WRITING

Part 2, Informal letter (CB page 100)

1 Read this Writing task.

This is part of a letter you have received from an English friend, who is planning to visit your home town next month.

> ... Of all the bad luck! I can't believe you're going to be away the week that I'm coming to visit. I haven't managed to find a hotel yet so I was wondering if you could recommend any (cheap) places to stay ...

Write a **letter** in reply to your friend giving your suggestions. (Write approximately 250 words.)

2 Read the mark scheme for the task. This will tell you what the examiner is looking for in an ideal answer.

> **Content (points covered):** the letter should contain greeting/thanks for last letter; the letter must mention two or three options for budget accommodation, possibly with prices.
>
> **Organisation and cohesion:** the letter should be divided into clear paragraphs, e.g.
>
> > paragraph 1 – greeting and reaction to any news in the letter
> > paragraphs 2/3 – options for accommodation
> > paragraph 4 – ending.
>
> **Range:** should use language suited to an informal letter to a friend (e.g. contracted forms are acceptable here); should use language for making suggestions and giving advice (e.g. *you could try + -ing ...*, *what about ...*).
>
> **Register:** informal.
>
> **Target reader:** would be informed about suitable places to stay.
>
> **Accuracy:** should not contain major errors that lead to misunderstandings or have a negative effect on the reader.

3 Now read the answer on page 59 and do the questions below.

1   Look at the list of points to include in Exercise 2 **Content**. Has the writer answered the question?

2   a) Has the writer organised the letter appropriately? Use the paragraph organisation in Exercise 2 to help you decide which paragraphs could be joined together.

    b) Does it begin and end appropriately?

3   a) Read the letter carefully and try to create a more informal register by introducing as many contracted forms (e.g. *I will = I'll*) as you can.

    b) How does the writer use punctuation to create informality? Tick (✓) the example you can find.

4   Find the following errors and make the necessary corrections:

    inappropriate use of a formal verb (*para 3*)
    incorrect use of a preposition (*para 3*)
    spelling mistakes (*paras 3 and 4*)
    incorrect use of an article (*para 5*)

4 Now write a similar letter of your own.

Dear Lois,

1 Thanks for writing back so quickly. I am very sorry about the mix-up with the dates. I thought you were not coming to Athens until the following week when I will be back from my trip.

2 Never mind. I will try to help you now.

3 I have placed a call to a number of hotels for you and the cheapest price is around twenty pounds a night. The nicest one is Hotel Victoria — a business contact of my father's stayed there and it has good breakfasts! — and it is in the centre near The Plaka so you can visit this place by foot. If that is too expensive then you could try a youth hostal for about 12 pounds a night.

4 There is one just around the corner from my house called 'Swingers'. I do not know anybody who has stayed there before but the owner showed me the room and it looks clean. The only problems may be that there is no ensuit bathroom and it may be noisy at night!

5 Please let me know if either option sounds the good one. If you can call me before Friday or send me an email then I can book it for you.

6 I would advise you to book your room in advance. Athens is a very safe city but as you will be a woman on your own it is better to be safe than sorry!

With love from

Krisoula

xxx

PS My mother and father send their regards to you!

Honesty, the best policy

READING
Part 3, Multiple choice (CB page 102)

1 Read the following article from a newspaper. Now answer the multiple choice questions **on page 61** by circling the best answer, **A, B, C or D.**

Are we living in a walk-on-by society?

Today how many of us seeing a group of 11- or 12-year-olds vandalising a phone box or picking on a younger child would actually intervene? Yet if we don't, who will?

Intervening would be an example of 'active citizenship', in which citizens should become guardians of their own communities, confronting disrespect and disorder. Instead of asking for more and more policemen on the beat, we should take minor law and order into our own hands.

Frankly this strikes me as unrealistic to the point of lunacy. In a highly disciplined society – Japan, for instance – you might well get away with rebuking someone for anti-social behaviour. But this is because the Japanese have a very highly developed sense of respect for authority.

I remember sitting in a subway train in Kyoto and noticing, to my surprise, that a young man sitting opposite me had put his feet up on the seat without removing his shoes (which the Japanese invariably do). As a foreigner, and with limited Japanese, I did not even think of rebuking him. But he caught my glance, obviously read my unspoken thought, blushed and removed his feet. Try anything like this on the London Underground and you might find that even an unspoken, but obvious, thought will call forth a torrent of the foul-mouthed abuse that has become such a notable feature of our society.

We all have at the back of our minds the notion that we are entitled to make a 'citizen's arrest'. But I have never met anyone mad enough to try a citizen's arrest – and with

good reason. If you get your facts wrong and jump to a hasty conclusion that the man lying on the ground is the victim when he actually started the fight, so that you seize the wrong man, then you could be guilty of 'false arrest' and be liable to damages.

Given that criminals are very ready to assert their 'rights', even against their victims, only a criminal lawyer or an off-duty policeman could arrest someone without fear of getting into serious trouble.

So, what would you do if, walking through the local park one day you notice two children who are obviously playing truant. Would you simply ignore them and then moan about the problems of truancy later to friends, or take a firm hold of their collars and march them to the police station. Or what if you saw a man hitting a woman in the street, you are bound to feel honourably called upon to intervene. But what if it is a lovers' row, and they both turn on you?

Surely there are times when we have to do something. What if you hear a woman scream in a side street and it sounds like a scream of terror, then what else can you do but try to help? The French actually have a stern and strictly enforced law that makes it a criminal offence if you fail to assist someone in danger or distress.

Our trouble is that we are an undisciplined society, in which we increasingly use the law to try to regulate fairly minor anti-social behaviour. The result is that many people feel that to be active citizens is to go along with an increasing busybodiness that is actually deeply unpopular.

How many of us would really want to report a motorist (let alone rebuke him) for a minor parking offence? Do not most of us feel that the police are already too keen to prosecute car owners, so that if we help them we feel less like 'active citizens' than collaborators. The paradox is that it is in societies which by our standards are not so organised that people are much more willing to intervene.

In Cairo a few months ago, coming out of a restaurant, I was approached by three ragged boys begging for money. They were obviously just about to snatch my wallet and run off when two passersby on opposite sides of the street bellowed at them in a real fury, and sent them on their way. I doubt this would happen in London. But in Cairo everyone smokes on trains and buses, everyone drops masses of litter and everybody hates the police.

A few years ago an elderly, publicly spirited woman I know saw a well-built mugger snatch a handbag from a girl on the Underground. She followed him down the escalator, found him standing on a platform waiting for a train, marched up to him and said: 'Young man, give me that handbag.' He was so startled that he meekly handed it over.

Then she really did behave like an active citizen: 'You will now come with me upstairs and we shall find a policeman and he will arrest you.' 'Ma'am,' he replied, 'don't push your luck.' This is what I would say to anybody prepared to take these ideas of active citizenship too seriously.

1 How did the writer react to the sight of the man on the train?

A He asked him to take his feet off the seat.

B He was embarrassed by his behaviour.

C He didn't say anything.

D He told him off for not removing his shoes.

2 The writer feels that

A we should be asking for more policemen.

B we should be prepared to deal with small law and order problems ourselves

C active citizenship works really well in Japan.

D the idea of active citizenship is inappropriate in England.

3 Making a citizen's arrest

A is something we often have on our minds.

B might lead to somebody other than the criminal being punished.

C could lead to the wrong person being found guilty.

D is only carried out by criminal lawyers and off-duty policemen.

4 Compared to the French, the British are less likely to intervene because

A they don't want to be unpopular.

B they can't be bothered.

C there is no law to make them do so.

D they can leave it to the police.

5 Which statement is closest to the writer's opinion?

A Cairo is less organised but people are more likely to intervene.

B Cairo is more organised but people are more willing to intervene.

C People in Cairo hate the police as much as the British.

D People have similar attitudes in both cities.

6 How did the writer feel about the actions of the elderly woman?

A She expected too much.

B She was foolish to intervene.

C He was surprised by what she did.

D He thought she acted bravely.

2 Complete these sentences by using the verb which collocates most strongly. All of the collocations are used in the text opposite.

1 You should .... your facts straight before you accuse me of lying.

2 Don't .... to the wrong conclusion. She's just a good friend.

3 Beth's a real bully. She's always .... on the other children in her class.

4 I was just about to ring you. You must have .... my thoughts.

5 I've just had my wallet .... by a gang of youths.

6 That phone box has been .... yet again. How am I going to make that call?

7 Even though it is tempting it can be dangerous to .... the law into your own hands.

8 That woman at the door looked a bit suspicious so I .... her on her way.

VOCABULARY

Phrasal verbs and nouns/adjectives from phrasal verbs (CB page 104)

1 Match the phrasal verbs (1–10) with their definitions (A–J).

1 lay something out ....
2 cry out against something ....
3 wear somebody out ....
4 rip somebody off ....
5 zip up ....
6 hand something out ....
7 drop in ....
8 come in ....
9 black out ....
10 climb down ....

A cheat somebody
B lose consciousness
C tire somebody
D disapprove of something
E distribute something
F fasten
G enter
H visit
I change your mind about an original opinion
J arrange something

2 Make a compound word from the phrasal verbs in Exercise 1 to complete these sentences. The first one has been done as an example.

1 I couldn't see what the thief had on underneath his .....zipped-up... jacket.
2 I can't believe Veronica paid over two hundred pounds for that dress. What a .... !
3 With this map we should be able to understand the .... of the building.
4 People on low incomes are forced to rely on .... from the government or charities.
5 The .... flight from Amsterdam has been delayed due to security problems on board.
6 There was a public .... when the Prime Minister made those comments about the unemployed.
7 The debate on animal rights ended in a humiliating .... on the part of the main speaker.

8 Your grandmother should see a doctor if she continues to have those ....
9 Haven't you noticed how pale and .... Kelly is looking?
10 One of the facilities available for the young people in the area is a .... centre with sports and other leisure facilities.

More informal expressions with *be* + particle (CB page 104)

3 Use the prepositions in the box to complete the sentences.

| in down off out up |

1 I'm a bit .... at the moment but I'm sure I'll cheer up soon.
2 That chicken's been in the fridge for over a week now. It's probably ....
3 I'm .... all day today if you need to contact me.
4 Frank can't reply to your email – all the computers are .... in the office.
5 My three-year-old niece is really naughty. She's always .... to no good.
6 Are you .... to go on that trip to Germany?
7 Competition entries must be .... by September 30th.
8 The fashion magazines say that flat shoes are .... this summer, so everyone will be buying them.
9 The book about the president's affair is finally .... in paperback.

ENGLISH IN USE

Part 1, Multiple choice cloze

1 Always look out for collocations (words that go together) in the multiple choice exercise. Underline the most appropriate word in each of the sentences below.

1 The police arrived within minutes at the *spot/area/scene/place* of the crime.
2 Amanda said that she would have no *concerns/worries/feelings/qualms* about reporting a crime to the police.
3 The victims of the burglary were given five hundred pounds by their insurance company in *recompense/reward/payback/award* for the damage to their house.

4 The youths who vandalised the college and stole three computers *posed/disguised/pretended/concealed* as students to gain entry.

5 Would you *close/turn/show/wink* a blind eye if you saw a crime being committed?

6 When Terry discovered his camera had been stolen he *reported/told/said/informed* it to the police immediately.

7 Many criminals feel no *distress/regret/apology/ remorse* about their actions.

8 Bill doesn't realise the *gamble/risk/bet/chance* he is running by not declaring his earnings.

9 Hundreds of pounds' worth of *gifts/treasures/ valuables/goods* were taken from the office.

10 The sooner that villain is *placed/put/taken/moved* behind bars the better.

2 For questions **1–15**, read the text below and then decide which word (A, B, C or D) best fits each space. Put the letter you choose (**A–D**) in the gap. The exercise begins with an example (**0**).

TOMORROW'S CRIMINALS

In the time it takes you to read this article, it is **(0)** C certain that two events will have taken place on a very large **(1)** .... indeed. The first of these certainties is that many crimes, mostly **(2)** .... but some serious, will have been **(3)** .... . Crime has been an **(4)** .... fact of life for many centuries and it is **(5)** .... to say, will continue to be so for the **(6)** .... future.

The second undisputed event is that our world will be populated by hundreds, even thousands, of new human beings, arriving bloody, screaming and kicking, and opening their eyes to **(7)** .... the future. Inevitably, some of these new-born babies will grow up to become the adolescents and adults who steal from cars, **(8)** .... houses, mug people late at night, **(9)** .... fires, rape, and kill.

And the million-dollar question is: Which of these new-born infants will become tomorrow's criminals? There are **(10)** .... predictors that can give us some **(11)** .... . Firstly, antisocial childhood behaviour, including misbehaviour at school, dishonesty and aggressiveness. There is a higher chance of the child **(12)** .... to crime if there is a history of criminality in the family, including **(13)** .... parents and delinquent older siblings. Family poverty is also a contributing **(14)** .... , whether it be due to low family **(15)** .... , large family size or poor housing. Poor parental child-rearing behaviour, including harsh and authoritarian discipline, poor supervision, parental conflict and separation from parents also play their part.

0	A totally	B utterly	C absolutely	D surely
1	A scale	B size	C area	D grid
2	A silly	B trivial	C stupid	D small
3	A done	B committed	C made	D tried
4	A unpreventable	B unstoppable	C unchangeable	D inescapable
5	A secure	B correct	C safe	D sure
6	A predictable	B expected	C known	D foreseeable
7	A face	B confront	C attempt	D achieve
8	A rob	B burgle	C thieve	D steal
9	A start	B commence	C set	D light
10	A enough	B number	C scores	D several
11	A clues	B help	C tips	D guesses
12	A moving	B tending	C turning	D going
13	A condemned	B convicted	C tried	D prosecuted
14	A fact	B factor	C circumstance	D instance
15	A income	B incomings	C wage	D payments

LANGUAGE STUDY

Nominal clauses in indirect speech (CB page 106)

1 Look at this extract from an announcement by the Managing Director of a company. Match the reporting verbs below to the sentences they correspond with. The first one is done as an example.

( ) remind   ( ) insist   ( ) warn   ( ) admit
( ) complain   (1) explain   ( ) conclude   ( ) point out

> 'Well, the latest figures don't look good. (1) Sales have been extremely poor over the past few months and (2) our overseas investors have refused to continue offering financial assistance. Nevertheless, (3) we have absolutely no intention of making any staff redundant at this stage. As I told you at the last meeting, (4) we still have orders to keep us going until well into the beginning of next year. Obviously, (5) if the situation doesn't improve soon we may have to look at our staffing levels. Unfortunately, (6) the Government aren't giving us the assistance we need. (7) If interest rates continue our situation is going to get worse. All I can say is (8) we need to be prepared for some difficult times ahead.'

2 Rewrite the sentences using the appropriate verbs.

Other verb patterns after reporting verbs (CB page 107)

3 Rewrite the following sentences using the reporting verb given.

1 'I'll do the washing up if you like.'
   He offered ....

2 'You should try that new supermarket on the main street. It's fantastic.'
   He advised ....

3 'Why don't you see a doctor about that cough?'
   She suggested ....

4 'I really don't agree with the idea that we should make people do military service.'
   I don't believe ....

5 'This Government will not give in to terrorist demands.'
   She insisted ....

6 'Get out of the car and empty your pockets.'
   He ordered ....

7 'OK. I suppose I did drive a little too fast last night.'
   She admitted ....

8 'All right. I'll get it done by tomorrow.'
   He agreed ....

9 'But I haven't borrowed your pen!'
   He denied ....

10 'I'm sorry, but I don't want to work this weekend.'
   He objected ....

Verbs with two objects (CB page 112)

4 Use a word from each column (**A–D**) to create sentences. How often can both 'indirect + direct object' and 'direct object + *to/for* + indirect object' be used?

Example: The police gave him directions.
   The bank lent her money/money to her.

A	B	C	D
police	play		promotion
jacket	show		visa
guide	give		suit
customs	lend	him/her	money
bank	make		record
DJ	cost		directions
tailor	offer		fortune
boss	refuse		exhibits

5 Find and correct the mistakes in the following sentences.

1 Could you suggest me a good film?
2 Can you explain me how this works?
3 'Where's my pen?' 'You lent him it.'
4 These are the files that accounts want. Can you send them them?
5 Hi Sam! Can I get for you a drink?
6 The photos of the baby came out really well. Who shall we send them?
7 I wrote to my friend a letter.
8 Could you give that magazine me for a moment?
9 I bought for my mum a bunch of flowers.
10 Our car causes for us so many problems. We need a new one.

ENGLISH IN USE

Part 2, Structural cloze

1 Being able to identify which type of word is missing from the text is essential in the structural cloze. Find examples of each of the following in the sentences below.

(modal) auxiliary *be/have/will/must*, etc.
preposition *in/at/on*, etc.
conjunction *when/so/because*, etc.
pronoun *me/it/them*, etc.
relative pronoun *who/which*, etc.
determiner *the/some/each*, etc.

1   You should .... called if you knew you were going to be late.
2   Excuse me? Have you got .... light please?
3   Do you really believe .... all that astrological stuff?
4   .... the weather was horrible, we had a great time.
5   Could you do .... a favour please? Pass me the salt.
6   That's the film .... received such terrible reviews, isn't it?

2 Other types of words that are commonly omitted are adverbs, particularly when they form part of a set expression. Complete the following sentences with the appropriate adverb.

1   Your essay was really well organised but you made .... a few mistakes.
2   We .... ever go out at weekends.
3   It is .... as well I came back to check. I'd left the door unlocked.
4   I've told you .... and over again. Don't take my car without asking!
5   She's by .... the best actress I've ever seen.
6   He didn't come into work again today. Worse .... , he didn't telephone in.
7   We invited John and Sheila as .... as June and Kelly.
8   The exam was really hard yet .... so they all passed.

3 Complete the following article by writing the correct word in each space. Use only one word for each space. The exercise begins with an example (**0**).

BOGUS 'YOUTH' TRICKS SCHOOL

At (**0**) *least* two inquiries are being held after it was revealed that a 32-year-old man has spent the last year pretending to be a pupil at a well-known Scottish school. Strathclyde Council is holding an immediate investigation into (**1**) .... the man, calling (**2**) .... Brandon Lee, apparently managed to spend three terms in the sixth form at Brearsden Academy (**3**) .... arousing the suspicions of classmates or teachers. The University of Dundee, (**4**) .... offered Lee a place to study medicine, is (**5**) .... holding an enquiry. Lee obtained five A grade passes in his examinations. The school (**6**) .... also be holding an enquiry, if (**7**) .... into the eyesight of some of Lee's teachers. The pupil had attended the (**8**) .... school seventeen years previously but several long-serving members of staff failed to recognise him. When he applied to attend the school, Lee presented documents showing that he had been studying at another school but had moved (**9**) .... the area. So (**10**) .... , no one knows his motive for pretending to be a pupil. However, (**11**) .... has been discovered that twelve years ago he began a medical training course at university but was asked to leave (**12**) .... failing his exams. Lee's true identity was revealed while he was on holiday in Spain. After an incident in a bar, the police (**13**) .... called by a hotel manager and found out that he had two passports, (**14**) .... for a seventeen-year-old and the (**15**) .... for a man nearly twice that age.

Making a living

READING
Part 2, Gapped text

1 Read the following article from a newspaper. Six paragraphs have been removed. You must choose which of the paragraphs A–G on page 67 match the numbered gaps 1 6. There is one extra paragraph which does not fit in any of the gaps.

The **Pressure** point
Stressed out? Don't fret, enjoy it!

I recently gave a course on stress, which had nothing to do with stress management. It said that stress is magical and needful to our inner lives. This is a very unfashionable idea. Everyone knows that stress at work is the disease of our time. That it can kill. That it should be avoided at all cost by stress management techniques such as visualisation of calm scenes, aromatherapy and yoga.

1

In peace and war, stress has turned ordinary people into heroes and heroines. It can galvanise and inspire. Those who actively seek stress know the value of it, so why does current thinking suggest that we should avoid it?

2

Yet the word 'stress' is used to refer to both cause and effect, to what makes people feel stressed and to how they feel when they are stressed. Because of this conflation of stimulus and response, arousal has come to be blamed for the harm caused by threats and dangers.

3

This isn't necessarily so, although it may happen. Animals, for instance, subjected to long-term, uncontrollable pain and threat eventually resign themselves to their fate and then succumb to disease. This behaviour has been labelled 'learned helplessness' and human research supports this theory. Helplessness causes changes which affect the immune system and make the body more susceptible to disease.

4

The unsatisfactory scientific research into stress has had two consequences. First, it has led to the medicalisation of the normal stress response, turning a survival mechanism into a disease. Second, it has led to a lucrative, underqualified and largely unregulated industry of stress counsellors, offering to 'manage' and manipulate stress arousal and make it go away. An industry that says both overwork and underwork can be 'stressful'. An industry whose techniques have been questioned by a number of scientific investigators as to their effectiveness and their purpose. An industry that encourages people to be calm about real threats they face at home and at work, when they should be getting off their backsides and doing something to help themselves.

5

There is one pattern to them all. Arousal, increasing tension and exhilaration leading to a resolution of the experience. By these activities we learn to survive. They toughen us up and help us to cope.

Yet nowadays, while every emphasis is placed on stressing the body to achieve physical fitness, stressing the brain is avoided. We are into mind flab in a big way.

6

A The problem here is not stress arousal, but failure to act on it. Doing nothing about a threat is clearly linked in the research literature to disease. Despair can be an anaesthetic but it is also a killer.

B In my course we look at society's training exercises for dealing with danger and actually go through with the arousal experience. Spectator sport, fairground rides, quizzes, thrillers and chillers of every kind, childhood dares and daredevil pursuits.

C Recently, I have been looking at the research on stress. Disturbingly, I found no agreed definition of the term. Stress arousal is a response to threat or challenge.

D My course was rather different. It featured clips from the climaxes of horror films, interviews with sports stars, creepy-crawlies (I have a giant metal spider named Esmerelda) and lots of evidence from the arts and sciences on stress arousal as the key to peak experiences.

E Lamentably, if we see somebody working flat out on a project, the fashion is to say 'they'll kill themselves'. How sad and strange. In reality, triumphing over adversity can give people a tremendous sense of achievement.

F The experimental literature on stress and disease is also prone to another serious error. It says 'disease often follows stressful experience, so stress must cause disease.' In logic, this is a flaw known as *post hoc, ergo propter hoc* – which means that 'it followed it, therefore it was caused by it'.

G Third, it is my view that in the triumph over terror we find our greatest rewards. Such experiences help us to become mature and independent.

---

2 Complete these sentences using the correct form of the word in CAPITALS.

1 I would like to complain about the .... service I've received from your company. SATISFY

2 Because she had only completed two years of her university degree they said she was .... for the post. QUALIFY

3 It is hard to trust hypnotherapy because it is an .... profession. Anybody can do it. REGULATE

4 The pressures of the job became too much for David and he began to experience an overwhelming sense of .... HELP

5 I'm not babysitting for my nephews again. They are .... CONTROL

6 The critics praised the .... performance of the two leading actors. MAGIC

7 Finding a cure for cancer would be a great .... for modern science. ACHIEVE

8 Short hair is never .... It rarely looks out of place. FASHION

3 Look at the way the word in *italics* is spelled in each of these sentences. Put a tick (✓) if the word is correct and if the word is wrong, write in the correct spelling. (All of these words appeared in the text.)

1 Stress is a *desease* associated with modern living. ....

2 When people feel helpless or are in long-term pain, they become *susceptable* to illness. ....

3 A large number of people appear to *sucumb* to illnesses associated with stress. ....

4 *Counsellors* are people whose job it is to help others cope with stress. ....

5 It is important to *acheive* one's goals and ambitions. ....

6 Healthy people are those who indulge in a number of different *activities*. ....

7 Some sceptics (including the writer) have *questionned* the view that stress is a bad thing. ....

8 Some scientific *investigaters* are disapproving of the stress 'industry'. ....

Tip: If you want to improve your spelling you could focus on the following areas when you are reading: double or single consonants?; suffixes (e.g. *-er/-or*? and *-ible/-able*?); and the 'i before e' rule.

VOCABULARY

Compound adjectives (CB pages 115/116)

1 Match one word from Column **A** with one from Column **B** to make compound adjectives.

A	B	
over	made	1 ....
part	employed	2 ....
computer	man	3 ....
one	literate	4 ....
well	style	5 ....
hand	term	6 ....
self	time	7 ....
traditional	time	8 ....
over	known	9 ....
long	anxious	10 ....

2 Use appropriate compound adjectives from Exercise 1 to complete the following sentences.

1 Applicants for the job are expected to be .... , particularly in word processing.
2 The chief executive of the rail company is .... for his ability to motivate staff.
3 The property for sale is a .... three-bedroomed house in need of some modernisation.
4 I know your first day at work will be nerve-wracking but try not to be ....
5 Beatrice has been absent from work for the last three months due to a .... health problem.
6 Most of the staff are happy to work .... as the extra money comes in useful.
7 Rita gets much more job satisfaction since she gave up working for the company and became a .... accountant.
8 For a special gift you could buy some charming .... souvenirs to take back home with you.

9 At the moment Harry is just a .... business but he's hoping to take on more staff next year.
10 Poppy has just enrolled on a .... course at college for 6 hours a week.

Prepositions

3 Complete the two short texts below by writing in the correct prepositions. Most of these expressions are in the Coursebook.

WANTED!
Manager for Housing Department

Are you a leader (1) .... the field of housing policy? Looking (2) .... the future?

You may be a graduate (3) .... any social science subject. You should have the ability to work (4) .... pressure, often (5) .... a tight deadline and be able to show a commitment (6) .... the needs of the homeless. Fluency (7) .... a language other than English will be an advantage. Please apply in writing, stating dates when you are available (8) .... interview.

Dear Tim,

Just started my new job working (9) .... the homeless. Housing is quite an interesting line (10) .... work to be (11) .... even though it has its frustrations. I'm (12) .... to my eyes in paperwork at the moment and seem to be working my fingers (13) .... the bone! Seriously, I'm working flat (14) .... on a report that has to be (15) .... on Monday morning. Oh well, I'll just keep going (16) .... automatic pilot ...

Phrasal verbs to do with work

4 Use your dictionary to find out the meanings of the following verbs.

suck   drift   stamp   thrive   aspire
chew   rank   beaver

5 Use one of the verbs in Exercise 4 in the correct form to complete the sentences below.

1 Stephen spent his twenties .... about from one job to the next without any real ambitions.

2 I'd watch out if I were you. Can't you see that Tony .... to being head of your department.

3 I hate the way Ron's always trying to .... his authority on his colleagues.

4 I need a little bit of time to .... over your ideas before I can comment on them.

5 Zoe doesn't seem to suffer from any stress. It's as if she .... on hard work.

6 Is Marie still .... away on her computer? I'll tell her to take a break soon.

7 Martin .... among the best of the new graduates.

8 Don't try .... up to the new boss. He can't stand people who creep.

ENGLISH IN USE
Part 5, Register cloze

Strategy

There are often words in the text needing to be completed that give you a clue to the word required. These are words that collocate with the missing word. Pay particular attention to verbs that precede the gap.

1 <u>Underline</u> the correct word in each pair in the following sentences. The first is done as an example.

1 Those interested in attending the party are asked to make a(an) <u>*contribution*</u>/*offering* towards the cost.

2 We were given the *impression*/*sense* that you intended to cancel your account.

3 Delegates were not able to come to any *agreement*/*consent* and concluded the meeting early.

4 Members will be invited to give their *opinions*/*views* at the meeting.

5 Should the product meet with our *requirements*/*demands*, we will forward our order to your sales department.

6 It is necessary to take into *consideration*/*contemplation* the cost involved in expanding the company.

7 A number of well-known bands will be making a(an) *appearance*/*show* at the concert.

8 The extension to the theatre is expected to be near *completion*/*finishing* this summer.

2 Read the memo below and use the information in it to complete the numbered gaps in the formal letter. The words you need do not occur in the memo. Use no more than two words for each gap. The exercise begins with an example (**0**).

MEMO

To: John Owen, Office Manager
From: Stella Bowen, Staff Training Manager
Subject: Edinburgh Conference

Just a brief note about what has been decided about the conference in Edinburgh which is coming up soon and that some people want to go to. Can you put these points in a formal letter to be sent to everyone? Firstly, up to ten people can go and those who have not been to a conference before are most likely to be chosen. They have to let the Personnel Manager know – a letter will do – before the end of the month – that's just ten days away. The really important thing is that employees must pay for everything first and will then be given all the money they have spent when they get back here. Obviously, they must get and keep written evidence of whatever they spend. Also, remind people that they have to write something about the conference for the rest of us to read.

LETTER TO ALL STAFF

(0) ...*Members*..... of staff who are **(1)** ....
attending the **(2)** .... conference in
Edinburgh should note that the following
(3) .... been taken. A **(4)** .... ten
places are available and **(5)** .... will be
given to those who have not attended a conference
on a **(6)** ....
Please inform the Personnel Manager in
(7) .... if you wish to go. Please do this
(8) .... days of the date of this letter. It is
important to note that those who attend the
conference must pay all **(9)** .... in advance
and will then receive a full **(10)** .... on
(11) .... to the office. Consequently, it is
absolutely vital that you obtain **(12)** .... for
all items of expenditure. Bear in mind that you are
(13) .... to write a report on the conference
for your colleagues to read.

LANGUAGE STUDY

Writing complex sentences (CB page 123)

1 Rewrite the following sentences using the word in CAPITALS. Make one sentence if possible and pay attention to punctuation.

1 I went out. It started to rain. MOMENT
2 He won the 100 metres. He came second in the long jump. ADDITION
3 The company has expanded in East Asia. It has consolidated its position in Europe. MOREOVER
4 He passed his exam. He didn't do any work. EVEN
5 The car hasn't been going very well. I think we should still try the journey. NEVERTHELESS
6 There has been talk that the President is unwell. He has never been fitter. CONTRARY
7 They hadn't had a holiday for a few years. They decided to go abroad. SINCE
8 They had two players sent off. They won 3–0. DESPITE
9 The house had locks on all doors and windows. The burglar still got in. SPITE
10 We admit to being slow to respond to your letter. We have done all we can. WHILE
11 The bodywork is in terrible condition. The engine's as good as new. WHEREAS
12 Sally's doing really well at school. Jamie doesn't seem to like it at all. CONTRAST
13 I've been taking the medicine. I don't feel all that good. ALTHOUGH
14 You've all worked extremely hard today. You can leave early. AS

2 Join the sentences below with the correct connecting word. Sometimes you will need to make changes to the sentences.

1 despite/in contrast
2 in spite of/moreover
3 because/therefore
4 however/on the contrary
5 although/in contrast
6 on the contrary/nevertheless
7 in contrast/whereas
8 nevertheless/therefore

1 Steve has been working at the company for almost 15 years and his work record is excellent. He has suffered from several illnesses over the past year.
2 He has continued to be one of the most popular members of the team. He contributes immensely to staff morale.
3 Colleagues have been willing to help with his work during periods of illness. He is very popular.
4 Unfortunately, there hasn't been any sign of improvement. He has seemed to get worse in the past month.
5 Colleagues have been keen to help out in the past. They are no longer able to deal efficiently with the extra work involved.
6 I appreciate that the company has not been employing new staff recently. I feel we need to appoint a part-time clerical worker to cover for Mike and allow him the chance to take extended leave.
7 This will hopefully enable him to fully recover. If he struggles on in his present condition the situation is unlikely to improve.
8 Steve is a valued member of staff. I strongly recommend we employ someone part-time.

ENGLISH IN USE

Part 4, Error correction

1 As you saw in Unit 1, the error correction task sometimes requires you to identify an extra and unnecessary word in a line. Underline the extra word in each sentence and identify what *type* of word it is. There are two of each type.

Example: Thanks, that is the most kind of you.
   .....quantifier...

1 I've got a friend who he met the Prime Minister.
   ....
2 Because the exam started late so we were given an extra 10 minutes. ....
3 The suspect entered in the building and escaped through a rear window. ....
4 He remembered that he hadn't been turned off the lights. ....
5 I'm really not enough satisfied with the service.
   ....
6 The pollution is a problem that governments must pay more attention to. ....
7 The view is much more prettier than I'd thought.
   ....
8 Although we arrived a bit late yet we still saw the beginning of the film. ....
9 You can't have read that magazine. I'm still looking at it. ....
10 We took more time answering the question than it was allowed. ....
11 He went on hiking during his last holiday in Scotland.
   ....
12 It's so heavy traffic for this time of day.
   ....

2 Some but not all of the lines in the following text contain one extra word that should not be there. Read the text straight through to find out what it's about. <u>Underline</u> the unnecessary words and tick (✓) the lines that are correct. The exercise begins with two examples (**0**).

How to be a Good Manager

0	✓	A lot of research has been carried out into what makes a good
0		manager. This research has covered <u>over</u> all types of working
1		environments by including industry, retailing and government.
2		As the result has been that several characteristics have been
3		identified as are being typical of the very best managers. It seems
4		that good managers are quick to give the praise to employees who
5		deserve it and also to pass it on when it comes from outside the
6		company, from a customer, for example. Also a characteristic of
7		good managers is that they treat every people fairly and do not have
8		favourites. The researchers found that managers who they were
9		thought to be discriminating against some people and giving to
10		others special treatment could seriously reduce the efficiency of
11		the work in force. It was also noticed that good managers moved
12		around a lot, for getting to know all the staff as well as people
13		outside the company, instead of always staying inside the office.
14		However, this had to be done carefully because employees, although
15		they appreciate the manager taking up an interest in their work
16		do not want him or her constantly be looking over their shoulder.

---

3 How many of the following appeared as extra words in the text? Tick them.

- pronouns
- determiners
- conjunctions
- auxiliary verbs
- prepositions
- adverbs

PROFITS

READING
Part 2, Gapped text

1 Read the following article from a newspaper. Six paragraphs have been removed. You must choose which of the paragraphs **A–G** on page 73 match the numbered gaps 1–6. There is one extra paragraph which does not fit in any of the gaps.

Stolen innocence

First Person

THE YOUNG POLICEMAN spoke in a monotonous tone and with an air of smugness. 'I have to inform you that your son has been arrested for theft.' It was a simple sentence, said perfunctorily, and it immediately changed everything.

1

As I drove to the police station, I tried to control alternating bouts of numbness and hysteria. I paced the reception area as I was told I must wait a further ten minutes to see my son. All I could think of was that he was only a few metres away from me, and that he needed his mother.

2

My son shame-facedly related the story. His friends had persuaded him to steal a pen from Woolworth's and after initial reluctance he had obliged them. While his incompetent initiation act was spotted immediately, his friends avoided being captured by the police.

3

His only answer to these repeated questions was to cry harder, and despite his misery I was not sorry for this. He had, after all, broken the law.

4

These conflicting thoughts went through my head as we endured the humiliation of finger-printing, mug shots and form-signing. As a first offender, my son was only given a caution and then allowed to go home. This meant he would be on police records until he was seventeen-years-old. Thankfully, he would not have a criminal record, but he had become a hidden criminal statistic.

5

But, paradoxically, I could not help feeling that this could be an effective deterrent. As a parent, I felt completely helpless and guilty. How could I ever get a perfect balance between discipline and affection. I decided that I should not shield my son from the consequences of his actions by trying to comfort him too much.

6

So did I.

A   At this point I finally gave in to the overwhelming need to hold my son and indulge in the emotional release we both wanted very much. My feeling of hurt and sense of betrayal were evident, as I kept asking my son why this had happened.

B   I did not hug my son again, even though I desperately wanted to. Just before we got out of the car, my son said with a poignant sense of finality, 'Mummy, I just don't feel the same any more. I feel changed now.'

C   As we drove home in silence, I looked at my subdued son. I did feel angry at the thought of him alone in a cell for over an hour. This obvious and unsubtle form of criminalisation outraged my maternal and humane instincts.

D   As I stood staring at him in shock, it slowly registered that he was talking about my eleven-year-old son – my defenceless, innocent child. The only thing that kept me vertical was the perfect certainty that my son would not, indeed could not, do this to me.

E   Although I was sure that this was an impulsive, one-off act of impulsive stupidity, I was nevertheless petrified by it. That sense of certainty about his integrity that I had taken for granted had gone for ever.

F   When I look back now, I still can't see any tell-tale signs that something like this was going to happen. I didn't realise he was hanging out with the wrong crowd until the policeman called.

G   At long last I was allowed to see my child, crumpled on the floor in the corner of a cell. His face was tear-stained. 'Of course you did not do it, did you?' I stated with all the confidence I could summon up. He did not reply but looked perceptibly much more desperate. In that second I realised the drama was over.

---

2 The style of the text opposite is rather formal. Match each formal expression (1–8) with its less formal equivalent (A–H).

1 nevertheless petrified ....
2 an initial reluctance ....
3 endured the humiliation of ....
4 it slowly registered ....
5 monotonous tone ....
6 consequences of his actions ....
7 the perfect certainty ....
8 related ....

A not wanting to at first
B boring voice
C a really sure feeling
D put up with feeling ashamed about
E it gradually dawned on me
F still really scared
G told
H result of what he's done

3 Choose the most appropriate expression in Exercise 2 to complete the sentences below.

1 The police promised to meet me at the scene of the crime but I was ....
2 Despite .... to invest further in their South American subsidiary, the company eventually proceeded with their expansion plans.
3 The writer .... some initially poor reviews and proceeded to win critical acclaim.
4 .... that I'd gone out and left the cooker on!
5 I'm not enjoying my history lectures one little bit. The tutor's got such a ....
6 A period in prison usually serves as an opportunity for the criminal to consider the ....
7 I did the exam with .... that I was going to fail.
8 So anyway, I .... him the joke about the elephant and the caterpillar, but he didn't even smile!

VOCABULARY

Prepositions and particles in phrasal verbs and other expressions

1 Complete these sentences with the correct preposition. You will have seen most of these phrasal verbs and dependent prepositions in the Coursebook.

1 Criminals can be broken .... into two distinct types – the hardened criminal and the opportunist.
2 Claire was able to pick .... one of the men who mugged her in an identity parade.
3 The young lads were arrested .... suspicion .... murder.
4 The police were tipped .... by an anonymous phone-caller, who didn't feel at all guilty .... reporting the suspicious behaviour.
5 The gang were all found guilty .... assault and sentenced .... three months .... prison.
6 Prisoners are deprived .... their freedom, which, some people would argue, is enough of a punishment.
7 When the family of the deceased heard the judge's sentence they poured .... their frustration to the press.
8 People who stalk famous celebrities are usually obsessed .... their victims. (*2 possibilities*)
9 Is there any evidence that young people are turning .... crime more often?
10 Unless we catch him before he strikes again, there is a real danger posed .... this man.

Collocation – crime and punishment

2 Complete each pair of sentences below with the same missing word. Choose from the words in the box. You may have to change the form of the word.

law rap penalty punishment
sentence criminal make

1 a. The people in some American states have voted to bring back the death ....
   b. There are very heavy .... for people who drink alcohol and drive.

2 a. The defendant was given a life .... for the murder of the old lady.
   b. The judge passed .... after the jury had given their verdict.

3 a. The burglar had a very long .... record.
   b. Don't try and approach that man – he's a hardened .... !

4 a. Corporal .... is no longer legal in the majority of schools in Europe.
   b. Capital .... is still carried out in many countries.

5 a. You shouldn't drive more than 70 miles per hour. It's against the ....
   b. The rioters went on the rampage showing little respect for .... and order.

6 a. I got a .... on the knuckles from my boss for being late for work three days running.
   b. You broke the computer, not me. I don't see why I should take the .... for your incompetence. (informal)

7 a. The teacher decided to .... an example of the girl found cheating in the exam.
   b. I'm going to .... you pay for that!

Collocation – adjectives formed from participles (CB page 131)

3 Complete these sentences using the correct form (ending in -ed or -ing) of the word in CAPITALS.

1 The rebels were believed to have killed hundreds of .... civilians. ARM
2 The government appears to hold .... beliefs about the punishment of young offenders. CONFLICT
3 After serving 15 years in prison for murder Louise is now a .... character. REFORM
4 The burglars had a fully .... out plan for the break-in. WORK
5 Although the thieves had taken all her jewellery, Diana's money had been left .... DISTURB
6 The police are making .... efforts to find the killers and bring them to justice. CONTINUE
7 Simon is now a .... solicitor in a law firm. PRACTISE
8 Doris suspected Earl of stealing her pen and gave him an .... look. ACCUSE
9 It turned out to be a very .... situation for the Board of Directors when the accountant was discovered defrauding the company. EMBARRASS
10 Most shops in the cities have an .... policy for dealing with shoplifting. ESTABLISH

ENGLISH IN USE
Part 5, Word formation

1 Complete the sentences with an adjective formed from the word in CAPITALS and one of the following affixes.

> **Suffixes:** -en -ive -ible -able -ly
>
> **Prefixes:** un- dis- in- im- ir-

1 After the attack the old man was left in .... care. INTENSE
2 It is not .... to walk the streets late at night by yourself. ADVISE
3 Those chocolates you brought back from your trip are simply .... RESIST
4 Try not to speak so .... about your parents. After all, they did a good job of raising you. KIND
5 When his marriage ended Daniel was left .... -hearted. BREAK

2 Look at the key word and complete the chart with as many forms of the word as you can. Make a note of which of the general and personal nouns can be made plural.

verb	general noun	personal noun
chair (e.g. a meeting)		
dance		
imagine		
administrate		
realise		
invest		
inform		
live		

3 Read the texts opposite. Use the words in the box to form one word that fits in the same numbered space in the text. The exercise begins with an example (**0**).

DETECTIVES FIND 'ALADDIN'S CAVE' IN PENSIONER'S HOUSE

Detectives making routine (**0**) ...*enquiries*........ into a completely unrelated matter were astonished at what they found in the house of an 80-year-old lady. Every room was stacked high with (**1**) .... goods which, over a period of twenty years she had taken from department stores. A police (**2**) .... said, 'No one suspected such a sweet old lady. She looks very (**3**) .... but she must have carried out several (**4**) .... every day. We found over 8,000 different items, so she was a pretty successful (**5**) ....' He added that, taking into (**6**) .... the lady's age, they had decided not to press charges but to let her off with a (**7**) .... The items would be given to charities.

(**0**) ENQUIRE	(**4**) THIEF
(**1**) STEAL	(**5**) SHOPLIFT
(**2**) SPEAK	(**6**) CONSIDER
(**3**) RESPECT	(**7**) WARN

PROTECT YOUR HOME NOW!

Are you confident your house is safe and secure? Do you have (**8**) .... locks to deter burglars? Do you have smoke alarms to give an immediate (**9**) .... that a fire has started? If you have any doubts, or think (**10**) .... can be made, then contact Praetorian Security without delay. Our (**11**) .... will carry out a free survey of your home and give you (**12**) .... on what needs to be done. There is no (**13**) .... to purchase any of our (**14**) .... but we offer free fitting on orders over £250 and a cast-iron five-year guarantee. In the (**15**) .... event of our security devices failing to keep burglars at bay, we will refund your money.

(**8**) EFFECT	(**12**) ADVISE
(**9**) INDICATE	(**13**) OBLIGE
(**10**) IMPROVE	(**14**) PRODUCE
(**11**) INSPECT	(**15**) LIKE

LANGUAGE STUDY

The passive (CB page 130)

1 Complete the following sentences with the correct form of the verb in brackets.

1 This letter must .... (*post*) today. You won't forget will you?

2 This letter should .... (*post*) yesterday. Why is it still here?

3 The company says it refuses .... (*intimidate*) by threats of strike action.

4 The company risks .... (*take*) to court for unfair dismissal.

5 The climbers said they were relieved .... (*find*) before night came.

2 In the following sentences the passive would be more appropriate than the active. Change the sentences and decide if the agent is necessary.

1 I'm afraid my company will have to make 300 people redundant.

2 Some people saw the robbers escape in a blue BMW.

3 The people in the court let the defendant sit during questioning.

4 Guests should vacate their rooms by 12.00 a.m.

5 The waiters serve lunch in the conference centre.

6 The bank will inform you of the changes as soon as possible.

7 He was relieved that he wasn't called up for military service.

8 The government may make drivers pay more for petrol.

3 Rewrite the following sentences using *it* + a passive construction.

1 Many people have often said that money doesn't bring happiness.

2 A lot of people fear that as many as 3,000 people have lost their homes in the flood.

3 Experts argue that people are eating far too much salt in their diet.

4 Some people in the TV company have suggested that the soap opera should be rescheduled

Reduced relative clauses (CB page 131)

4 Decide which sentence in the following pairs of sentences contains a reduced relative clause. Write *Yes* or *No*.

1 The people elected to do the job did really well. ....
The people elected John Andrews to do the job. ....

2 The woman rescued from the fire is recovering in hospital. ....
The woman rescued the child and is recovering in hospital. ....

3 The parents invited a magician to the party. ....
The parents invited to the party were asked to bring some food. ....

4 The director awarded the prize to his colleague. ....
The director awarded the prize was overcome with emotion. ....

5 Rewrite the following reports using reduced relative clauses where possible.

Report 1

A middle-aged man who was arrested yesterday for armed robbery has escaped from police custody today. The man was last seen driving off in a stolen Fiat and is described as extremely dangerous.

Report 2

A beach in the North West which is often used by local children has been found to be contaminated due to high levels of radioactive waste. It has been closed by the local council. Samples of soil that were taken by inspectors have been examined and appear to contain twice the acceptable level of radiation.

ENGLISH IN USE
Part 6, Discourse cloze

1 It is often the case that the extracts taken from a text consist of very similar structures. In this case particular attention needs to be paid to the logic of the text. Match the following clauses so that they make the most sense. The first one has been done for you.

1 We stayed in a beautiful hotel	A although it wasn't far.
2 I complained about the service	B although it didn't really need it.
3 I've decided to sell my car	C although I'm not comfortable using it.
4 I'm going to go abroad this year	D although it was really expensive.
5 We decided to get a taxi	E although I don't know why I bothered.
6 I was going to buy his computer	F although neither of us liked them.
7 He bought us some chocolates	G although I'm not sure where to go.
8 We decorated the kitchen	H although I don't think I'll get the amount I want.

2 Read through the following text and then choose from the list (**A–J**) the phrase which best fits each space (**1–6**). Some of the phrases do not fit at all. The exercise begins with an example (**0**).

A MISCARRIAGE OF JUSTICE

In 1968, Michael McDonald was arrested and charged with murder. He was tried, found guilty and sentenced to life imprisonment but he continually protested that he was innocent. Fortunately for him, capital punishment had just been abolished or he **(0)** ..J.. . He was surprised when he was found guilty, although he admits that the evidence presented in court suggested that he **(1)** .... . He complained about his lawyer who, he thinks, **(2)** .... . After Mr McDonald had been in prison for two years, a man confessed to a lawyer that he

had committed the murder. This man said that he **(3)** .... . Bound by professional confidentiality, the lawyer felt that he could not report the matter to the police. The man

who had confessed would not do so. Consequently, Mr McDonald remained in prison, where he **(4)** .... . After ten more years had passed the real murderer died peacefully and at last his lawyer went to the police and Mr McDonald was released. Many people might think that the lawyer **(5)** .... . Then Mr McDonald, who had committed no crime, **(6)** .... . If that had happened then Mr McDonald would have been released after two years, although even that is a long time to spend in prison when you are innocent.

A	would have complained	**G**	might have escaped
B	should have known the truth	**H**	would not have spent so long behind bars
C	should not have been	**I**	could have committed the crime
D	should have tried harder		
E	should be in prison and not Mr McDonald	**J**	might have been hanged
F	should have acted earlier		

WRITING

Part 2, Discursive essay

1 Read this writing task.

> In your English class you have been discussing the pros and cons of putting surveillance cameras in public places as a way of preventing common types of street crime. Write an **essay** on this topic. (Write approximately 250 words.)

2 Read the mark scheme for the task. This will tell you what the examiner is looking for in an ideal answer.

Content (points covered): the essay must explain what surveillance cameras are; must discuss reasons for and against their use; should give a personal opinion.

Organisation and cohesion: the essay should be divided into clear paragraphs, e.g.

> paragraph 1 – introduction to the topic, background information
> paragraph 2 – pros
> paragraph 3 – cons
> paragraph 4 – concluding remarks, personal opinion.

Range: should use language suited to a discursive essay and for discussing advantages/disadvantages, as well as weighing up opinion (e.g. *On balance it could be argued that …*).

Register: fairly formal.

Target reader: would be informed of the writer's view on this topic.

Accuracy: should not contain major errors that lead to misunderstandings or have a negative effect on the reader.

---

3 Now read the answer on page 79 and do the questions below.

1 Has the writer answered the question? Tick off the list of points in Exercise 2 **Content**. What extra factual information has he included that would make a good impression? Highlight it and put a tick (✓) next to it.

2 Has the writer organised the essay appropriately? Divide the essay into sections and mark each one with 'advantages' and 'disadvantages'. Where does the writer give his personal opinion?

3 Underline the expression that the writer uses to introduce the other side of the argument and put a ✗ next to it.

4 Find the following errors and make the necessary corrections:
   incorrect use of determiner (*para 1*)
   incorrect use of present tense (*paras 1 and 2*)
   incorrect use of adjectives/collocations (*para 2*)
   incorrect word order (*para 3*)

4 Now write your own answer to this question.

SURVEILLANCE CAMERAS – MEDICINE OR POISON?

1 Surveillance camera are common in Britain. About 300,000 more than in every other country, watching people all over the United Kingdom, according to 'Privacy International', a data protection organisation. Since last year 150 of these cameras (placed in the London district of Newham) have a very special feature: They are connected to a police computer which compares the faces of pedestrians with wanted criminals. If the computer detects a similarity of at least 80 per cent it alerts the police.

2 This example shows the main reason for surveillance cameras – the fight against crime. But if one looks at the criminal statistics then it is clear that the British crime rate shows no difference to other western states without strong surveillance. Obviously the advantage of surveillance cameras is very low. These cameras probably only have two effects: First of all the citizens have the illusion of more security; secondly, the politicians are able to say 'Look, we do something against crime.'

3 The flip side of the coin is doubtless a loss in two key features of liberal democratic states: freedom and privacy. But what is the value of democracy if the citizens become more and more the spied-upon subjects of the state? Perhaps it sounds cynical to crime victims but in my opinion a liberal democracy without crime is impossible. Like everything has this society advantages and disadvantages but I think the advantages predominate. This does not mean that the state should stop the fight against crime but this fight should happen within the framework of a democratic society and not against this society. I am convinced that the majority of citizens would prefer a free liberal democracy with crime instead of a closed society without crime where everyone is a subject under surveillance.

UNIT 11

A sense of belonging

READING

Part 1, Multiple matching

1 Read the magazine article on page 81. Match each statement (1–14) with the person (A–E) in the text to whom it refers.

Which person or persons			
was able to live on the island only after finding a job there?	**1**		
have an administrative role on the island?	**2**	**3**	
found it difficult to get on with other children?	**4**		
do not mind difficult weather conditions?	**5**	**6**	
has a job involving animals?	**7**		
feels the lack of privacy?	**8**		
realised the benefits of the island only after leaving?	**9**	**10**	
leads a solitary existence?	**11**		
was able to help construct the place where she lives?	**12**		
was introduced to the island by her parents?	**13**		
realised where she wanted to live as soon as she saw it?	**14**		

A	Sue Ward
B	Christine Hopkins
C	Jilly Lo-Vel
D	Linda Williams
E	Mary Squires

Now match the features described in the text (15–21) with the name of the island (A–D). You may choose an island more than once.

Which island	
has one inhabitant most of the time?	**15** ....
has a dozen inhabitants?	**16** ....
has no cars?	**17** ....
has educational opportunities?	**18** ....
is very windy?	**19** ....
has a connection with money ?	**20** ....
has been inhabited for hundreds of years?	**21** ....

A	Sark
B	Papay
C	Ramsey
D	Lundy

In my heart this is
where I want to be

Of the six hundred and sixty-four islands around the coast of Britain, one hundred and twenty-six are inhabited and many of those who live on them couldn't live happily on the mainland. 'Some people need island life,' says Sue Ward, who is warden of Ramsey, a rugged island off the Welsh coast. She is usually alone on the island, but never lonely. 'I suffer loneliness in a crowd with people I can't talk to,' she says. 'But not here. Ramsey is where I belong. The island has a strong personality and, although it may seem arrogant to say this, I feel it likes me.'

This feeling is common among islanders. Christine Hopkins felt it the moment she set foot on Papay, a windswept but fertile island in north Orkney. 'I'd always loved Orkney, but here I felt immediately at home, although I never dreamed I'd be able to live here.' Islands seem to have a way of making room for those who live on them. Shortly after that visit, Christine spotted a job in a newspaper and for the last three years she has been the sole teacher in Papay School, with from two to five pupils in her charge.

Jilly Lo-Vel has from early childhood had a passion for Lundy, a small island in the Atlantic. Her father, an artist, first visited the island in 1947 after finding a Lundy island coin with a puffin on it – the island is full of these birds. He and his family were enraptured by the immense cliffs, heathery uplands and deep valleys. Jilly met her husband Reg on the Lundy Gannet, the island supply boat, and they have been two of the island's twelve permanent inhabitants for eight years, looking after visitors and breeding and selling Lundy ponies. 'Lundy,' says Jilly 'has a special magic.'

But for Linda Williams, the island that beats all others is Sark, which she first visited twenty-three years ago and where she has lived ever since. 'I came to Sark on a day trip and knew at once that I wanted to make my home here.' Now she lives in a house she and her husband built in the lush centre of Sark and serves as one of the twelve elected members of the Sark Parliament. Since 1565, the people of Sark have ruled themselves, adopting some mainland laws and rejecting others. Change comes very slowly. Incomers with modernisation schemes have little chance. Sark remains free from cars, street lights, tarmac roads, golf courses, airport and purpose-built hotels.

But do children appreciate the idyll of an island childhood? Mary Squires grew up on Lundy, where her father was an administrator. As the only child on the island, her greatest friend was a pet goat and she spent her days swimming and playing with her father's sheepdog. Her clothes were chosen from a mail order catalogue. 'It was idyllic, looking back, but at the time it seemed normal.' Only when she was sent to boarding school on the mainland did she begin to appreciate what she had left behind. 'I'd learnt to love my own company, so I hated the girls at school, and they didn't like me much. I'd long for the holidays.'

Island life isn't everyone's idea of an idyll. Too isolated. And island life is expensive – prices of goods tend to be much higher by the time they have travelled from the mainland and choice is limited too. Gossip is difficult to escape from. 'If you haven't done anything, people make it up,' says Linda Williams. On visits to London, she relishes anonymity.

No wonder islanders caution those thinking of moving from the mainland to spend a winter on an island first. For you must relish the hardships. 'There are so many areas of life over which human beings have total control, but that doesn't apply here on the island,' says Linda Williams. 'It's good to be at the mercy of the weather and cooking gets more exciting when food is running short.' And Christine Hopkins looks forward to the long winter evenings on Papay. Last winter, with some neighbours, she studied in the evening by using the school's satellite system to receive a course being given in Aberdeen. Now she is learning to make Orkney strawback chairs and teaching herself how to make felt. Indeed, islanders are nothing if not resourceful. We may think of them as escapist or whimsical but they are formidably realistic, enterprising and resourceful.

2 Complete the following sentences with the correct adjective formed from the word in CAPITALS. All of these words appeared in the text.

1 We have to be .... about the chances of winning the next tournament. REAL
2 When I first saw the island I was completely .... by the wonderful view. RAPTURE
3 The village I visited is so peaceful – in fact, it's quite .... IDYLL
4 The hillside was wild and .... WIND
5 The council discussed the .... plan to improve facilities at the sports centre. MODERNISE
6 You have to be quick-thinking and .... to be good at many jobs. RESOURCE
7 The oldest .... of the town often remember how life was in the good old days. INHABIT
8 The people most suited to making lifestyle changes are those who are clever and .... ENTERPRISE

VOCABULARY

Phrasal verbs (CB pages 145/149/150–151)

1 In each of the following sentences underline the correct particle.

1 Although they'd had their holiday booked for some time their plans fell *back/in/through/out* at the last minute and they were forced to cancel.

2 The city where I grew *into/on/out/up* was really bustling.

3 Lorraine's fed up of trying to earn a living as an actor. She'll probably give it *away/back/in/up* for a more secure job.

4 Sorry, but I don't have enough money with me to pay this bill. If I put in £7.00 could you make it *in/into/out/up* to ten?

5 They've just bought a house on an island in Scotland. In winter they're often cut *across/down/off/out* from civilisation.

6 Hundreds of small villages were wiped *away/ down/off/out* during the hurricanes.

7 If you're going to succeed in this job you'll have to learn to get *along/around/back/together* with your colleagues a little better.

8 Almost all children go through a phase of wanting to run *along/away/off/out* from home.

9 Let's go for a brisk walk along the hilltop. That should really blow *away/back/off/out* the cobwebs!

10 The situation's fully under control. We'll only ask you to come *between/by/in/on* if we need you.

Places to live

2 Match each of these words from the Coursebook (1–8) with their dictionary definitions (A–G).

1 mansion ....   5 council house ....
2 shack ....   6 trailer ....
3 lodge ....   7 farm ....
4 hut ....   8 housing estate ....

A country house or cabin for use in certain seasons in the year

B small roughly-built house or shelter (×2)

C area of land including buildings used for growing crops or raising animals

D caravan or other container that is pulled by a truck

E large and stately house

F large area of land with houses built on it

G low-cost home built by the local authority and rented to low-income families

3 Choose one of the words from the list in Exercise 2 to complete each sentence.

1 During the winter months Paula and her family often stay in a skiing ....

2 Tom makes his livelihood from a small number of pig- ....

3 Before I could afford to buy my own house I rented a ....

4 Peter hooked the .... to the back of the car and set off for his holidays.

5 You should see the size of her house – it's nearly as big as a .... !

6 The local council has plans to develop another .... in order to tackle the housing shortage in the area.

7 The poet works in a wooden .... in the middle of the forest where he is guaranteed peace and quiet.

Prepositions

4 Complete the following sentences with the correct preposition.

1 When Sue saw the state of the flat she was going to be living in she gasped .... horror.

2 The service in the hotel that Betty was staying in was .... her worst nightmare.

3 Even though Millie is quite well-off her feet are still firmly .... the ground.

4 Bob is extremely glad to be back .... full-time work after a long spell of unemployment.

5 The first time that Colin lived abroad he was homesick .... English food.

6 .... the heart .... the city centre you'll find the swimming pool and art gallery.

7 There isn't anything to do in my home town during the evenings – it can only be described .... rather dull and boring.

8 If you travel out of season you'll be able to go on holiday .... a fraction .... the cost.

9 Travelling alone means that you can enjoy having the pleasure .... your own company.

10 David is taking part .... a scheme to get more volunteers involved in the local community.

ENGLISH IN USE

Part 1, Multiple choice cloze (CB page 145)

1 Underline the most appropriate word in each of the following sentences.

1 After selling up her home and leaving her job in England, Miranda was ready to *desert/emigrate/leave/migrate* to Australia.

2 Brian and Phillipa have established a(an) *blooming/enlarging/growing/thriving* business selling office equipment.

3 I can tell you've been somewhere hot for your holiday. Your hair's been *bleached/brightened/whitened/yellowed* by the sun.

4 There has been a reversal of the *fashion/indication/movement/trend* in driving cars in favour of using public transport.

5 Moving to another city for the first time is a brave step to be *doing/going/making/taking*.

6 Hazel's life on the farm is a far *cry/yell/shout/scream* from her career as an accountant.

7 Travelling around the world and living a different lifestyle is certainly character-*building/developing/forming/shaping*.

2 For questions **1–15**, read the text below and then decide which word, **A**, **B**, **C** or **D**, best fits each space. The exercise begins with an example (**0**).

PERMACULTURE CLUB

Today Cindy has decided to (**0**) .A. 100 trees. When she came here, this place was no different from any other in the state of New South Wales. Once covered with trees, it had been (**1**) .... for farmland. Without trees, Australian earth is eroded. During the rains, roads are (**2**) .... away and the rivers are red with earth.

A Texan by birth, she met Graham, an English graduate, when they were working in the United States. 'We were two kids with a (**3**) .... . We wanted to live off the land without (**4**) .... it, and only produce what rubbish we could (**5**) .... with ourselves.' Two years later, they were riding across Australia on a motorbike, looking for a (**6**) .... of land. When they saw the (**7**) .... hillside in New South Wales, they knew this was it. The farmer was happy to sell. Eroded and (**8**) .... , the valley was no use to anyone. After paying the farmer, they were (**9**) .... with 100 dollars, a saucepan and a change of clothes. There was no (**10**) .... so they had to sleep outside. It was the (**11**) .... of summer, with temperatures around 40 °C.

In the beginning, Cindy knew nothing about horticulture. 'We started planting with ten packets of seeds we'd brought. We just planted everything anywhere, all together. The (**12**) .... is that plants, animals and people do better if they live together. Mixed planting (**13**) .... a system in which there is more wildlife, better soil and better crops that are more (**14**) .... to damage by pests. Cindy admits it is (**15**) .... intensive but she has saved one tiny corner of Australia.

0	A plant	B sow	C seed	D dig
1	A cleared	B removed	C cut	D severed
2	A soaked	B washed	C flooded	D watered
3	A prospect	B image	C hope	D dream
4	A hurting	B breaking	C damaging	D wasting
5	A deal	B do	C make	D act
6	A part	B piece	C section	D field
7	A bare	B naked	C plain	D blank
8	A sterile	B barren	C fruitless	D dead
9	A left	B remained	C over	D changed
10	A cover	B protection	C shelter	D refuge
11	A height	B peak	C top	D summit
12	A belief	B idea	C conception	D objective
13	A causes	B originates	C gives	D creates
14	A defensive	B resistant	C immune	D insensitive
15	A farming	B work	C labour	D effort

LANGUAGE STUDY

Creating emphasis through grammar
(CB page 147)

1 Complete the following sentences by putting a suitable word in each space.

1 .... surprises me is that a Government minister thinks they can get way with behaving so badly.

2 Having to pay tax on my wages and the goods that I buy .... what really annoys me.

3 .... is the way he presumes he can turn up late all the time without an apology that is so irritating.

4 The town .... we got married was recently in the news.

5 It was the way he spoke to her .... really surprised her.

6 It was a time .... all the members of the group were not really getting on with each other all that well.

7 .... you haven't told me is where you met each other.

8 The sudden decision to sell the company .... what shocked investors most.

2 Rewrite the following sentences using cleft sentences.

1 I really enjoy going out to restaurants.
Going ....

2 People who don't put the top back on the toothpaste really upset me.
What ....

3 Brazil have won the World Cup the most times, not Italy.
It ....

4 I get so angry at people who push in front of me in a queue.
People ....

5 You haven't paid me back that money yet.
What ....

6 The exam takes place in June not July.
It ....

7 I don't like having to do all the housework on my own.
What ....

8 I get fed up going to work during the dark winter mornings.
Going ....

3 Rewrite the following speech made by a Government Minister using cleft sentences to emphasise the points in *italics*.

Minister's speech

'This Government has spent millions on health and education since it came to power. *The leader of the Opposition fails to understand* that more people are getting treated in our hospitals under this Government. *This Government is determined* to increase the educational opportunities of the people of this country. *People who have little* are the concern of this Government. *The Opposition party* spent years ignoring the needs of the people, not us. We appreciate the needs of the people. *We don't treat them* with disrespect. *The Prime Minister was the person* who vowed to reduce unemployment. *This Government is the one* that has been successful in this endeavour. *The Government's only concern is the health and prosperity of our nation.*'

ENGLISH IN USE
Part 2, Structural cloze

1 Match the following words in Column **A** with a definition in Column **B**.

A		B
1 remote	....	A plant found in desert regions
2 mural	....	B isolated
3 lush	....	C a painting done on a wall
4 malnourished	....	D growing thickly and strongly
5 cactus	....	E delightful
6 thrive	....	F grow well
7 improvise	....	G do something without preparation
8 enchanting	....	H be underfed

2 Complete the following article by writing the correct word in each space. Use only one word for each space. The exercise begins with an example (**0**).

3 Which of the following types of words were missing from the text? Tick them.

- (modal) auxiliary *be/have/will/must* etc.
- preposition *in/at/on* etc.
- conjunction *when/so/because* etc.
- pronoun *me/it/them* etc.
- relative pronoun *who/which* etc.
- determiner *the/some/each* etc.
- adverbs *quite/often/just*
- adjectives *big/small/green*

LATIN PRIMER

Truckers who drive through the vast and remote Brazilian northeast often stop (**0**) ......*off*.......... at Cruzeiro do Nordeste. Not for very long. The town is (**1**) .... more than a couple of streets and a petrol station. But it is home to Arnaldo da Silva, a local artist who, amongst (**2**) .... things, paints murals on trucks.

(**3**) .... he is not painting lorries, Arnaldo likes to do landscapes. Several can (**4**) .... seen painted on the wall in the Cruzeiro's only restaurant. The wall paintings are of lush greens and deep blues; palm trees, rivers (**5**) .... big they look like oceans, waterfalls, fishermen and ducks.

They are pure fantasy: it hardly (**6**) .... rains in Cruzeiro do Nordeste; many of (**7**) .... 639 population are malnourished; cactus is the (**8**) .... plant that thrives. 'There is no water here', explains Arnaldo. 'That's why I like painting it.'

An hour's drive north is São Jose do Egito, (**9**) .... has attracted many visitors – mainly academics. Together (**10**) .... the nearby towns of Teixeira and Itapetim, (**11**) .... forms a triangle which is the centre of Portuguese improvisational poetry.

No one is sure (**12**) .... the culture sprang up in a region (**13**) .... poor and remote as this, (**14**) .... it is believed to have arrived with French or Arab immigrants centuries ago. The poets work (**15**) .... pairs and compose according to strict form. 'The poems are so rich, so enchanting, that the people love it,' says poet and schoolteacher Charliton Patriota.

WRITING

Part 2, Brochure (CB pages 152/153)

1 Read this writing task.

> The school, college or university where you are studying has arranged a two-week visit from a small party of foreign students from an English-speaking country. The visitors will be attending classes during their stay. You have been asked to write a brochure which will be sent to them in advance of their visit in which you welcome them and give them advice about studying at your home institution. Write your **brochure**. (Write approximately 250 words.)

2 Read the mark scheme for the task. This will tell you what the examiner is looking for in an ideal answer.

> **Content (points covered):** the brochure must include a welcoming message, and three or four main areas of practical advice, e.g. directions for getting around; facilities available (library, computers, leisure, food/drinks); what to expect in the classroom; where to go for further help; what to do in the evenings.
>
> **Organisation and cohesion:** the brochure should be divided into clear sections, each with their own heading. Some ideas are:
>
> > 'Welcome to …'
> > 'Finding your way around'
> > 'Entertainment'
>
> **Range:** should use language suited to a brochure i.e. describing places (*The college is situated in …*); locations (*You can find the library on the second floor*); and giving advice or making recommendations (*For a cheap mid-morning snack why not go to … ?*).
>
> **Register/tone:** semi-formal, with a warm and friendly tone, i.e. addressing the reader directly (*If you want to use the computers while you are here you'll need to get a special pass*) is preferable to a more formal style (*The computers can be accessed on production of a student pass*).
>
> **Target reader:** would be interesting to the reader and raise anticipation of the visit; should provide enough information to reassure him/her about any worries.
>
> **Accuracy:** should not contain major errors that lead to misunderstandings or that have a negative effect on the reader.

3 Now read the answer on page 87 and do the questions below.

1 Look at the list of points in Exercise 2 **Content**. Has the writer included all the useful information? Put a tick (✓) in all the places where you think she has offered good practical advice.

2 a) Look at the suggestions for organising the brochure in Exercise 2. Has the writer organised the brochure appropriately?

  b) Think of a suitable title for the brochure and add this to her answer.

3 Does the writer achieve the appropriate register? Does she use mainly active or passive forms, for example? What effect does the use of exclamation marks (!) achieve?

4 Find the following errors and make the necessary corrections:
  incorrect use of definite article (*para 2*)
  incorrect preposition of place (*paras 3 and 4*)
  spelling mistake (*para 4*)
  incorrect sentence construction (*para 4*)

4 Now write your own answer to this question.

1

Welcome to our visitors from Scotland.
We are very pleased that you are able to make this exchange with St George's College!

Accommodation/food

2

You will stay in a hall of residence along with our regular students. Each room has a bed (of course!), a wardrobe and a desk for study. There is a small bathroom in your room, which it is cleaned every two days. There is also a fridge but your main meal will served in the canteen at 1 p.m. each day. You need to use the tickets that you are given — just give them to the staff in exchange for your food. If you want coffee or any other type of drink you can get it from the machines on every floor of the college but you need to have the small change.

Studying at St Georges's College

3

When you arrive to the college you will be given a 'study buddy', which is a friend who will be your guide for the two weeks. You will have a tour of the college and we are proud of our library, which is one of the largest college libraries in Budapest. There is a computer lab and you can have free access to Internet as long as you don't spend too much time sending emails! The timetable begins at 8 a.m. but it is a tradition in our college that class does not start until quarter past eight. If you have to miss class you should explain to your teacher afterwards.

Evenings

4

Please do not stay to your room every night. On Wednesdays there is shown a film that is usually American with Hungarian subtittles. On Thursdays we have an English Club that meets to the Room A7.

5

We hope you enjoy your stay!

Calamities and mishaps

READING
Part 3, Gapped text (CB pages 162/163)

1 Read the following article from a newspaper. Six paragraphs have been removed. You must choose which of the paragraphs **A–G** on page 89 match the numbered gaps **1–6**. There is one extra paragraph which does not fit in any of the gaps.

High risk factors

There is nowhere in Britain as hellish as the high plateau of the Cairngorms in bad weather in winter. Fierce winds and biting cold sap your strength and deep snow can threaten avalanches. When the sky and snow-covered mountains merge, expertise with map and compass is essential to avoid disaster on the featureless terrain. So the safe return of Jacqueline Greaves this week after surviving two nights in arctic conditions was little short of a miracle. Most climbers who know the area hadn't expected she would be found alive.

1

Jacqueline Greaves survived because she had four things going for her. She was experienced, well-equipped, had the mental toughness essential for survival – and she was lucky. Other climbers this winter have not been so fortunate.

2

The northern slope of Ben Nevis can be just as savage as the Cairngorms. Navigating down from its summit in bad weather is notoriously difficult, with dangerous slopes on three of its four sides. It might seem an unlikely arena for enjoyment but climbers will drive all night from London to spend a weekend on the icy gullies and steep walls, which are famous throughout mountaineering.

3

Their decision seemed prudent and you might think that they were saving the rescue services an unpleasant night's work looking for them. Except that the two men were off-duty members of the RAF Search and Rescue Team – the team that found Jacqueline Greaves – and most of the other people in the hut were also mountain rescuers.

4

There are around twenty fatalities each year on the hills of Scotland, a number that has altered little in the last ten years despite the increase in the numbers climbing and walking. This figure includes those who suffer heart attacks while out walking. But the number of accidents is increasing fast, putting great pressure on rescue teams and threatening fundamental changes in how they operate.

5

Below Ben Nevis, the town of Fort William has become a major centre for growing numbers of outdoor enthusiasts who come to ski, climb and walk. Donald Watt, leader of the Lochaber Team, watches them with a wry smile. They are potential clients, but he doesn't preach. 'We are the same people. My hobby is climbing – it always has been. We aren't rescuers, we're mountaineers who do rescues. People can be stupid and when they are, we'll say so, but we all do it at one time or another.'

6

Neither Donald Watts, nor the other members of his team, like this idea but it may be a change that is inevitable.

A I do not know if I met William Murphy the day before an avalanche swept him to his death on Ben Nevis. All I know is that two weeks ago, high on Ben Nevis with a climbing partner, we met two Irishmen. They too were retreating down the mountain in bad weather and we shared out hot tea. They told us enough of themselves to make me think, when I saw the story of how Murphy had been killed, that our paths had so briefly crossed. Spend much time climbing and you start believing in fate.

B These people, who care for the injured and carry the bodies down, love the mountains and being in them as much as those they help. They may be more cautious because of what they have seen and they are certainly aware of the pain suffered by distraught relatives. But they understand the basic principle of climbing and hill-walking: that something that gives such immense rewards and joy can also demand a terrible and sometimes unavoidable price.

C Just below the summit of Ben Nevis is a small mountain hut. Soon after speaking with the two Irish climbers, we were back inside the hut, where there is a short-wave radio. As we talked, it suddenly came to life. Two climbers on a route high above told us through the raging wind that they were turning back.

D Yet the increase in incidents is enough to make Donald Watt contemplate privatisation in the more popular areas like the Cairngorms and

Lochaber. 'I shudder to think about it but it might happen. We're looking at the Alpine situation, where rescues are done by a professional organisation.'

E The Lochaber Mountain Rescue Team is one of the busiest in Scotland. It had forty-four call-outs last year, mostly for leg injuries to hill-walkers. Like all the other twenty-three Scottish teams, it is run by volunteers and almost all the money it needs is raised through voluntary contributions, charity events and gifts from grateful survivors.

F People regularly go missing in the Cairngorms, all too often without the happy ending of this latest incident. Earlier this winter, experienced climber Jane Thomas died of hypothermia after a navigational error left her too exhausted to continue. A few years ago, five schoolchildren and a teacher died after being overcome by a blizzard in the same area.

G Her remarkable survival is due to her vast experience of climbing and having the right equipment with her. She also had a reasonable supply of food, enough to keep her going. She did exactly the right thing – digging a hole in the snow and sheltering there until the storm died down and the rescuers could find her – and she was fortunate that they did.

---

2 Underline the best word in the following sentences. The words you need appeared in the text opposite.

1 I'd think very carefully before spending all your money on a motorbike. It might be more *cautious/careful/prudent/hesitant* to set some aside for a rainy day.
2 Stella watched Anthony trying to fasten his bulging suitcase with *funny/wry/ironic/witty* amusement.
3 Our *fundamental/important/elementary/original* concern is to make sure that the children have somewhere safe to play.
4 You shouldn't keep criticising your younger sister. It really *weakens/saps/reduces/takes* her confidence when you run her down.
5 It was a(an) *brutal/violent/unkind/savage* attack by his friend's dog that left Chris with those terrible scars.
6 It was a difficult *terrain/condition/earth/ground* for cycling – really wet and muddy.
7 You're in no position to *lecture/say/scold/preach* to me about dangerous driving when you always drive beyond the speed limit!
8 People are urged to be careful about swimming in the river. This year there has been a record number of swimming *calamities/fatalities/killings/destructions*.

VOCABULARY

Phrasal verbs

1 Complete the following sentences with the correct form of the words in the box.

| round   turn   pull   hand   take   protect   cover |

1 Fortunately, the travel insurance that Gerald had .... out before leaving home meant that he was .... against the loss or theft of his camera.

2 The babies had their hats .... down over their heads to .... them from the bright sun.

3 The young suspects were .... up for questioning by the police and forced to .... over their possessions.

4 Gill is looking much slimmer now she's .... up exercising regularly.

5 The driver of the car .... out in front of the bus and caused a major accident.

6 The judge .... out a harsh prison sentence to the motorist found guilty of drinking and driving.

7 We were going to try and reach the peak of the mountain but the weather conditions forced us to .... back.

8 What would .... your holiday off nicely is a trip to see the lakes.

9 Thank you for the invitation to go snowboarding this weekend but I'm afraid I'll have to .... it down.

10 The firefighters .... their hoses on the source of the blaze in an effort to contain the fire.

Prepositions

2 Complete the sentences with the correct preposition. Try to learn the completed expressions.

1 There is a *question mark* .... whether Janice is able to leave hospital so soon. (*2 answers*)

2 Michelle was .... *despair* when her cat went missing from home.

3 Researchers are trying to discover why some people are more *susceptible* .... illness than others.

4 Whenever I'm at the gym I get irritated by the loud music that some people *insist* .... having.

5 The best form of exercise to *participate* .... is one which makes your heart pump .... *a rate* .... 120 beats a minute.

6 The accident happened because she was .... *the wrong place* .... *the wrong time.*

7 The climbers managed to *survive* .... drinking rainwater from the gullies.

8 Many of the walkers were *overcome* .... the blizzard and were forced to go back.

9 Tom is having time off work because he's *suffering* .... stress.

10 The number of people having accidents in the home *puts great pressure* .... the ambulance services.

11 Could you lend me some money? I left my wallet at home and I'm .... *a fix.*

12 Do you remember when Sam almost fell out of the tree and was left *suspended* .... *mid-air?*

Collocation

3 Underline the correct verb(s) in the following sentences. In each sentence there are one or two correct collocations.

1 This looks like a good place to *pitch/erect/put up* our tent. (2)

2 After that unfortunate accident Bill seems to have *done/made/taken* a full recovery.

3 Rail customers are able to *deposit/leave/put away* their luggage in our lockers. (2)

4 Scientists are still *carrying out/conducting/making* experiments into human cloning. (2)

5 Have you heard that the minister has *undergone/had/suffered* a heart attack? (2)

6 Mia *makes/takes/gives* no bones about the fact that she doesn't want to have any children.

7 I *shudder/shiver/shake* to think what might have happened if you'd got caught in the snowstorm.

8 The two friends have decided to *enter/participate/take part* in the boating competition. (2)

9 Beware of criminals *pretending/acting/posing* as door-to-door salesmen. (2)

10 Don't tell me again how dangerous motorbikes are. You've already *made/placed/stated* your point.

4 <u>Underline</u> the correct noun in the following sentences. You will find most of these collocations in the Coursebook.

1 In spite of their popularity it seems that many sports are actually a health *hazard/danger*.

2 If you witness a car accident you should telephone the emergency *brigade/services* immediately.

3 The tourists were kidnapped and held hostage in a five-day *ordeal/trauma*.

4 Can you give me some help? I seem to have got myself in a *fix/problem*.

5 The weather report has just issued a storm *caution/warning* so we'd better not go climbing today.

6 Jenny was involved in an unfortunate *event/incident* with the police when she was caught speeding in her car.

7 So Paul's broken his leg this time? That guy is so *accident/calamity* prone!

8 Driving through those country lanes when it's dark is an absolute *experience/nightmare*.

ENGLISH IN USE

Part 1, Multiple choice cloze

For questions **1–15**, read the text below and then decide which word, **A**, **B**, **C** or **D**, best fits each space. The exercise begins with an example (**0**).

THE SKYDIVER WHO FELL 1,000 METRES AND LIVED

Astonishingly, a skydiver whose parachute failed to open properly has (**0**) .A. a 1,000 metre fall to the ground, suffering only (**1**) .... bruising but no broken bones at all. This amazing story began when Martin Ford, who has over twenty years (**2**) .... of parachuting, took off in a Cessna aircraft with five (**3**) .... skydivers. Their plan was to practise (**4**) .... hands in a mid-air formation but when they left the aircraft Martin was involved in a (**5**) ..... with another skydiver and their parachutes became tangled. The (**6**) .... did not panic but, after falling together for 500 metres, managed to (**7**) .... . The other skydiver released his main parachute, opened the reserve and landed safely. Martin kept (**8**) .... and tried to do the same. But he was unable to do so because as he turned in the air the parachutes began to (**9**) .... themselves round him and he eventually (**10**) .... consciousness.

He landed in a field that had recently been ploughed, so the earth was quite (**11**) .... and cushioned his landing to some extent. He was (**12**) .... to hospital where a doctor commented, 'His survival is miraculous. Often in such cases there are serious internal (**13**) .... because when the body decelerates on hitting the ground, the internal organs continue moving. For example, the brain can strike the inside of the skull with some (**14**) ..... . But Mr Ford only has (**15**) .... physical injuries.'

0	**A** survived	**B** overcome	**C** endured	**D** resisted
1	**A** hard	**B** severe	**C** rough	**D** grave
2	**A** practice	**B** knowledge	**C** experience	**D** training
3	**A** associate	**B** colleague	**C** partner	**D** fellow
4	**A** connecting	**B** keeping	**C** touching	**D** linking
5	**A** collision	**B** crash	**C** impact	**D** bump
6	**A** team	**B** combination	**C** pair	**D** couple
7	**A** divide	**B** separate	**C** part	**D** split
8	**A** attentive	**B** aware	**C** quiet	**D** cool
9	**A** envelop	**B** wrap	**C** enclose	**D** cover
10	**A** surrendered	**B** left	**C** lost	**D** missed
11	**A** gentle	**B** smooth	**C** fine	**D** soft
12	**A** rushed	**B** hurried	**C** dashed	**D** sped
13	**A** breaks	**B** damages	**C** injuries	**D** wounds
14	**A** strength	**B** force	**C** energy	**D** power
15	**A** outside	**B** superficial	**C** light	**D** surface

LANGUAGE STUDY

Linking words – condition (CB page 161)

1 Rewrite the following sentences using the words given.

1 I won't call you if I don't hear anything. (unless)

....

2 You aren't 17 yet, so you can't drive a car. (if)

....

3 Guests are allowed to use the washing facilities. The room must be locked up when finished. (condition)

....

4 OK. You can borrow the car. But make sure you get it back before 8.00. (as long as)

....

5 The Government won't discuss the issue if there are any preconditions. (only)

....

6 You can't get into that club unless you wear a jacket and tie. (provided)

....

Linking expressions in informal written English

2 <u>Underline</u> the most suitable linking word or expression in the following sentences. In some cases both are correct.

1 *By the way/What's more*, did I tell you I've found a new job?
2 The mechanic told me it had a problem with the suspension *or something like that/or so*.
3 *By and large/All in all* it's a really good company to work for. But they don't really give you the chance to do much training.
4 Then after all that we got held up at customs for three hours. *To put it in a nutshell/To cut a long story short* we ended up missing the plane.
5 You know that new shop I was telling you about in town? *Anyway/Well*, apparently it's doing really well.
6 No I'm not lending you any money. *As a matter of fact/In fact* don't you still owe me some money from last week?

3 Complete the following extracts from informal letters using the linking expressions in the box.

well or something like that
to cut a long story short and that was that
as I said anyway in fact

1
> I haven't been able to concentrate on anything lately. (1) .... I'm finding any kind of work at all quite challenging. The doctor told me I was suffering from insomnia (2) .... , I can't remember the exact term he used. He didn't spend much time examining me; he just asked me a few questions (3) ....

2
> We're thinking of going to Spain this year. But we've had so many problems at home. Tom's not been well, Chris has been having trouble at work. (4) .... none of us fancied organising anything. (5) .... Chris is still getting hassle from her boss. He's insisting she takes her holiday later. (6) .... we've decided to stay at home. (7) .... I'd better be going. Bye.

Inversion

4 Rewrite the following extracts from a speech starting each sentence with the word provided.

1 I have never witnessed such behaviour.
Never ....

2 If the union hadn't been present at the meeting we would have all been made redundant.
Had ....

3 If we had known of their plans earlier we could have organised some form of resistance.
Had ....

4 We will not be satisfied until our demands have been met.
Not ....

5 We must on no account give in to their heavy-handed tactics.
On ....

6 We will only withdraw our threat of strike action when management agree to drop their proposals.
Only ....

ENGLISH IN USE

Part 3, Error correction

1 In most of the lines in the following text, there is either a spelling or a punctuation error. For each numbered line, write the correctly spelled word or show the correct punctuation. If there is no mistake in a line, put a tick (✓). The exercise begins with three examples (**0**).

<table>
<tr><td colspan="2" align="center">**Why should the sea-level rise if global warming causes the icecaps to melt?**</td></tr>
<tr><td>**0**</td><td>...floating..........</td><td>If the icecaps were flaoting in the sea, global warming</td></tr>
<tr><td>**0**</td><td>...melting would.</td><td>and the subsequent melting, would have no effect</td></tr>
<tr><td>**0**</td><td>............✓........</td><td>on the sea level. Think of a lump of ice in a glass of</td></tr>
<tr><td>**1**</td><td>.....................</td><td>water: it displaces only its own wieght in water, so</td></tr>
<tr><td>**2**</td><td>.....................</td><td>when it melts the level remains the same But the great</td></tr>
<tr><td>**3**</td><td>.....................</td><td>mass of the icecaps is not afloat. Only the arctic has a</td></tr>
<tr><td>**4**</td><td>.....................</td><td>large body of such ice. In Canada and Siberia, ice carpets</td></tr>
<tr><td>**5**</td><td>.....................</td><td>the land. Antarticas nearly fourteen million square</td></tr>
<tr><td>**6**</td><td>.....................</td><td>kilometres is covered by ice more than two kilometres</td></tr>
<tr><td>**7**</td><td>.....................</td><td>thick eighty percent of the world's fresh water. If the</td></tr>
<tr><td>**8**</td><td>.....................</td><td>icecaps melted tomorow, the sea would rise by about</td></tr>
<tr><td>**9**</td><td>.....................</td><td>eighty metres. But currant predictions say the next fifty</td></tr>
<tr><td>**10**</td><td>.....................</td><td>years will see a rise of twenty to thirty centimetres'.The</td></tr>
<tr><td>**11**</td><td>.....................</td><td>main course will be expansion of warming sea water. In</td></tr>
<tr><td>**12**</td><td>.....................</td><td>fact as temperatures rise, more water vapour forms.</td></tr>
<tr><td>**13**</td><td>.....................</td><td>Climatic models, suggest much of it will fall as snow</td></tr>
<tr><td>**14**</td><td>.....................</td><td>on the Antarctic, making it thicker? This may well</td></tr>
<tr><td>**15**</td><td>.....................</td><td>balance with the ice melting at the North pole, all of which</td></tr>
<tr><td>**16**</td><td>.....................</td><td>means that rising sea levels are highly unlikely to be a danger in the future.</td></tr>
</table>

2 Which of the following categories were the cause of mistakes in this text? Tick them. (See CB Unit 7, page 57.)

- capitals
- homophones
- full stops
- apostrophes (in contractions and possessives)
- final *e*
- natural pauses in sentences
- commas

- suffixes
- hyphens
- similar looking words
- *i* before *e*
- double consonants
- silent letters

13 The natural world

READING

Part 4, Multiple matching

1 You are going to read a magazine article about poisonous animals. Match each statement (**1–12**) with the numbered section (**A–F**) where each idea occurs.

Where do these ideas occur?	
What some people fear most.	**1** ....
Larger size does not mean greater toxicity.	**2** .... **3** ....
Advice to carry a drug that can prevent death.	**4** ....
How a creature deters attackers with a non-poisonous liquid.	**5** ....
The creature that causes the most deaths.	**6** ....
A creature that retaliates only when touched.	**7** ....
The ability of a poisonous creature to escape notice.	**8** ....
A creature that is extremely dangerous only in large numbers.	**9** ....
A creature that attacks without moving.	**10** ....
Disagreement among experts.	**11** ....
A creature that is extremely long.	**12** ....

Now match the characteristic (**13–18**) with the species (**A–F**).

none of these is poisonous	**13**	**A**	snakes
inflicts a long wound	**14**	**B**	bees
the seriousness depends on the part of the body attacked	**15**	**C**	fish
two dangerous ones have very different poisons	**16**	**D**	birds
dozens of members of this species are dangerous	**17**	**E**	scorpions
looks dangerous but is harmless	**18**	**F**	spiders

2 Complete the following sentences with the correct form of the words in the box.

camouflage   sting   flick   venom   swarm   bite   squirt

1 Have you heard how Mike was attacked by a .... of bees? He's lucky to be alive.

2 If you've been .... by a bee you should try to remove it with a fingernail or the back of a knife.

3 The eastern brown snake has a .... that could be fatal if you're not treated quickly.

4 The majority of snakes are able to .... themselves in their surroundings making it impossible to see them.

5 You can imagine how terrified I was when I saw the snake moving towards me .... its tongue in and out.

6 The scorpion protects itself when under attack by .... its poison at its predators.

7 One of the most .... creatures in the animal kingdom is the honeybee.

What's your POISON?

The encounter with a poisonous snake is the stuff of nightmares. But in many parts of the world snakes are the least of your worries. There are poisonous species in every major animal group except birds. Most are insects, fish or reptiles.

A

When most people think of a poisonous animal, it is the tongue-flicking snake that springs straight to mind – and with good reason. Of the three thousand or so snake species identified, four hundred are dangerous to humans and a few dozen are lethal. Specialists disagree over which snake is the most poisonous. The Australian taipan, the Indian king cobra, the African black mamba will all kill you – quickly. But after recent tests the Australian *Parademansia microlepidota* shot to the top of the toxicity charts. There is a big difference between the most venomous snakes and those most likely to bite you. Favourite for the greatest annual death toll is probably the saw-scaled viper, which is widespread from Africa to India. It is quite difficult to spot, being less than forty centimetres long and well-camouflaged. It is quite aggressive and – crucially – it lives in areas where people walk barefoot. Although its venom is not among the most potent, many victims die because of poor or non-existent medical attention.

B

For many, the fear of spiders ranks higher than that of snakes. While few spiders are life-threatening to humans,

their venom usually contains dangerous nerve-poisons that can paralyse breathing muscles, making breathing painful. It is rarely big spiders that pose real danger. In the USA, there are two particularly dangerous small spiders. One, the Southern Black Widow, has a bite which contains a nerve poison fifteen times more potent than rattlesnake venom. The other, the Brown Recluse, produces a very different venom which leaves the victim with a black gangrenous patch up to fifteen centimetres wide.

C

Scorpions belong to the same group as spiders – the arachnids. Their venom, which like spiders', is a nerve-poison, is stored in two sacs supplying a curved sting at the end of the tail. As with spiders, the scorpion's size and ferocious appearance are not good indicators of the danger it represents to humans. The whip-tailed scorpion of the southern states of the USA looks formidable but has no sting. Instead it squirts a fluid rich in vinegar which is sufficient to deter the lizards and skunks that are its predators. On the other hand, the North African fat-tailed scorpion is one of the deadliest. A sting from it produces a burning pain, then tingling, followed by sweating, racing pulse and rapid shallow breathing. Paralysis of the breathing muscles may occur, causing death.

D

The sea has its fair share of venomous inhabitants. Jellyfish are among the best-known, though of the thousands of species only a few dozen are hazardous to humans. Perhaps the best-known is the Portuguese man-of-war, though strictly speaking this is not a true jellyfish but a collection of many individuals. The colony floats partially above the sea surface, with its stinging tentacles hanging several metres below. Brushing against the tentacles causes a burning sensation, skin damage and sometimes fever, chills and muscle spasms. Quite a lot of swimmers have had an unpleasant encounter with this creature. Death is rare from Portuguese man-of-war stings, but more common after encounters with tropical jellyfish such as the box jellyfish and the sea wasp. Their venom is highly toxic, capable of stopping your breathing or heartbeat.

E

Of the ocean's twenty-five thousand species of fish, fewer than a hundred are dangerous to humans. Most injuries are caused by stingrays which explode into action if trodden on or handled by accident. The tail is whipped forward over the ray's back, and on the end is a vicious, barbed spine. If this makes contact, it not only produces a wound about twenty centimetres long, but the venom injected causes severe pain and nausea and may affect the circulatory and nervous system. Human fatalities, however, are rare. The most venomous fish of them all is the repulsive stone fish. This ugly fish lives on the sea-bed, camouflaged and immobile, usually against a rocky or coral background which it resembles. Sharp poisonous spines run along its back and fins, and each one is primed with two sacs of venom near the tip. The poison is extremely powerful, produces excruciating pain and attacks heart and breathing muscles, often resulting in death if the victim is not promptly given the antidote.

F

Curiously, the venomous creature responsible for most deaths is the honeybee. So-called killer bees are merely a very aggressive kind of honeybee. Widespread throughout the world, bees commonly live alongside humans and many people are allergic to their stings. The annual death toll worldwide is probably tens of thousands. Bee venom contains histamine, which in a healthy person produces only local inflammation and moderate pain. Attack by a swarm of bees is much more serious. Multiple stings produce greatly exaggerated symptoms, causing severe swelling, which may trigger a full-body allergic response, followed by death within hours. Even a couple of stings to mouth or throat can be dangerous as the swelling can hinder breathing. People who know they are allergic to bee stings should carry adrenalin to counteract the effects.

VOCABULARY

Collocation

1 Underline the correct word in the following sentences. All of these expressions are in Unit 13 of the Coursebook.

1 When we reached the town, there were no *gestures/indications/signals/signs* of life. It seemed deserted.

2 If you don't brush your teeth frequently then the mouth becomes a(an) *breeding/existing/living/working* ground for bacteria.

3 Some languages in the world have fewer than one hundred speakers and are becoming dangerously close to *ceasing/dying/ending/extinction*.

4 The doctor told Harry that he may seem healthy at the moment but if he continues to smoke he'll be living on *borrowed/lent/stolen/taken* time.

5 Industrial pollution has destroyed much of the planet's *actual/natural/normal/usual* environment.

6 The Orinoco crocodile is a(an) endangered *breed/group/species/variety* often hunted for its hide.

7 If I stand on this hilltop I can just about catch a *glimpse/look/show/sight* of the valley where I grew up.

8 There are many villages *inhabited/cohabited/resided* by only a handful of people.

Prepositions

2 Complete the following sentences with the correct preposition.

1 Debbie is rather partial .... a good cheese at the end of a meal.

2 Weightlifters, bodybuilders and other sportspeople should avoid using drugs .... all costs.

3 An allergic reaction may occur .... a few minutes of eating a particular food.

4 Legislation is needed to protect the rainforests .... further destruction.

5 From that distance it's easy to mistake a hare .... a rabbit.

6 Despite spending two hours underneath the snow the child was left relatively unscathed .... its ordeal.

7 Changes in the atmosphere will have a negative impact .... the health of the next generation.

8 Rescuers finally found the climber who was suffering .... exhaustion and hypothermia.

9 Standards in many holiday resorts are .... the decline.

10 There has been a drop recently .... the number of people who are taking adventure holidays.

Phrasal verbs

3 Use your dictionary if necessary to find out the meanings of these phrasal verbs from the Coursebook.

A	plunge into	G	give up
B	set up	H	throw away
C	tire out	I	wrap up
D	set off	J	go through
E	end up	K	die down
F	curl up		

4 Look at the word or phrase in *italics* in each of these sentences and replace it with the correct form of one of the phrasal verbs (A–K) in Exercise 3.

1 At the end of the evening we always *conclude by* .... going home in a taxi.

2 Mary decided to *sit down in her chair and relax* .... with a good book instead of watching television.

3 Make sure all packaging from this toy is *discarded* .... to avoid the danger of suffocation to young children.

4 The weather is rather chilly this morning so you need to *dress in warm clothes* ....

5 When the emergency services arrived at the scene of the car crash Jack had already been *left* .... for dead.

6 The noise from the party eventually *subsided* .... and the neighbours were able to go back to sleep.

7 We *began our journey* .... at four o'clock in the morning and didn't arrive until after seven that evening.

8 In order to take her mind off her personal problems, Billie *decided to get more involved in* .... her work.

9 You can imagine how *exhausted* .... we were the day after the party.

10 Jennifer is going to *establish* .... an organisation for people who have *undergone* .... similar experiences to her.

ENGLISH IN USE
Part 4, Register cloze

Read the following leaflet on waste prevention. Use the information to complete the numbered gaps in the informal letter to a friend. Use no more than two words in each gap. The words you need do not occur in the leaflet. The exercise begins with an example (**0**).

LEAFLET

WHAT CAN YOU DO TO PREVENT WASTE?

Waste prevention at the household level starts at the point of consumption by considering products and services with the least environmental impact. This requires individuals to make decisions based upon the amount of raw material and energy used to manufacture these products.

Some households in a town in Wales have reduced the amount of waste they produce by 90%, through the use of recycling. Paper and cardboard, glass bottles and jars, tins and cans are collected weekly for recycling, and organic kitchen and garden waste is collected for compost. A monthly collection is provided for any reusable items not catered for by the weekly recycling service, including furniture and paint. Wood is checked by a local carpenter before being distributed as firewood.

A refill scheme is provided for a wide range of household cleaning products, whereby a full bottle can only be purchased from a village shop on condition that an empty one is returned.

Waste is not looked at in isolation but tackled alongside other environmental problems such as agriculture, transport and consumerism. Thus the town's involvement with an organic farmer in the vicinity, where there is a vegetable delivery scheme to households, helps achieve local, sustainable production of nutritious food and the purchasing of that food in a completely packaging-free form.

INFORMAL LETTER

I've just been reading this interesting article on recycling. One of the things it argued was that the best way to (**0**) .....avoid...... having a load of waste is to (**1**) .... more carefully about the things we buy, and to use things that do the (**2**) .... to the environment. For example, we shouldn't buy things that (**3**) .... a lot of raw material to make them. Apparently there's a town in Wales that has (**4**) .... waste by about 90%. (**5**) .... they have a collection of most kinds of rubbish for recycling — and if they (**6**) .... certain things then, they have another one every month for other stuff that they can't get (**7**) .... And get this; you can't (**8**) .... some things from the local shop (**9**) .... you (**10**) .... back your empties. The town also does business with (**11**) .... organic farmer. It means people eat food that is (**12**) .... them, and it saves paper because it (**13**) .... packaging.

LANGUAGE STUDY

Participle clauses (CB pages 176/177)

1 Underline the correct form of the verb in the following sentences.

1 *Having had/Having* a shower I went to bed.

2 *Having put/Putting* his hand in his pocket he realised he had lost his wallet.

3 *Having bet/Betting* that his team would win the game, he was surprised to learn they had lost 6-0.

4 He called the police when no one answered the phone *having believed/believing* that there was something wrong.

5 *Having/Having had* nothing to do he decided to go to bed early.

6 *Having been arrested/Being arrested* six times previously for minor offences the youth was given a custodial sentence.

7 *Having realised/Realising* she had forgotten to call her husband she ran to the nearest telephone.

8 He left for work half an hour early *having been concerned/being concerned* that the traffic would be heavier than usual.

2 Rewrite the following sentences using present or perfect participles.

1 He fixed the car then went to work.

2 She felt a little sick so she decided to go to bed.

3 He sat down to watch TV after he'd washed the dishes.

4 He left early for work because he knew the traffic was going to be heavy.

5 Since he had agreed to do the job cheaply, he could hardly now refuse.

6 Clare gets her own way more often because she's the youngest child.

7 After the exam was finished the candidate admitted he had cheated.

8 As the weather wasn't very good they decided to stay at home.

3 Rewrite the following sentences starting with either a present or past participle. Make any changes necessary.

1 James, who was arrested for the recent post office robbery, is expected to be charged today.

2 The Olympic Games, which is held every four years, is arguably one of the world's biggest sporting competitions.

3 The students in Group B thought the teacher was going to be off sick and so stayed at home.

4 I have been sold a defective machine and demand a refund.

5 The fossil, which scientists believe to date back millions of years, is supposed to be one of the largest ever found.

6 The landscape, which was painted by the artist early in his career, shows a remarkable sense of proportion.

7 She decided to drop out of university once she had realised the course was of no interest to her at all.

8 The manuscripts, which were written in the 12th century, were expected to fetch more than £1 million in the auction.

4 Some, but not all, of the participle structures in the following account contain mistakes. Correct those that you think are wrong.

Aimed to fulfil a longtime dream, to meet some dolphins out in the wild, in March 1995 I flew out from New Mexico to Florida for two weeks. Having always been being fascinated with dolphins, I was really looking forward to getting to see them.

Joining Vicki, our captain, on her boat the day after our arrival we sailed out to sea. She began sending out her 'signature' – what dolphins use to call to each other, essentially their equivalent of names. Sounds emitting from an underwater speaker soon attracted a dolphin which lead us away from the island, took us about six miles out.

Finding four more together, we hung back at a respectful distance. Watching them surfacing and diving, the dolphins gave us a little show by playing with their fish. They'd surface with fish in their mouth, twist and contort their bodies, tossing the fish through the air. Knowing by Vicky since birth, Inga, a young dolphin seemed very eager to get close to us. Swimming around and around, sometimes back and forth right underneath the boat, we got close enough to her to touch.

LANGUAGE REVIEW 1

1 Underline the correct form of the verb in *italics*. Sometimes both answers are correct.

1 I *have to/must* go to the dentist on Friday. They've asked me to come in for a check-up.

2 My grandfather *used to/would* live on a farm and every summer we *used to/would* go down and visit him.

3 I *have been doing/have done* a lot of overtime lately. This week, for example, we *have been having/have had* a lot of orders for the new catalogue so I *have had to/had to* work till late all week.

4 They've decided to withdraw from this year's competition, *which/what* has really disappointed their supporters.

5 This is my brother Steve, *who/that* I was telling you about.

6 If you don't know the person's name just write 'to *whom/who* it may concern'.

7 I got to the party as soon as I could but it *had finished/finished* by the time I arrived.

8 Sorry, I haven't got my homework. I *had forgotten/forgot* to pick it up this morning.

2 Complete the following sentences by supplying the correct form of the verb in brackets. In some cases more than one answer is correct.

1 We are supposed .... (*wait*) until he gets back from the meeting before we make any decisions.

2 I prefer .... (*eat*) my dinner in front of the TV than at the dining table.

3 I think we would prefer .... (*see*) the film on Saturday rather than during the week.

4 I wish you .... (*argue*) with me all the time. Can't we just agree to disagree?

5 I don't know what's keeping her. She said she .... (*call*) as soon as she got back from her holiday.

6 He admitted .... (*be*) near the bank at the time of the robbery.

7 Their relationship .... (*say*) to be going through a lot of difficulties at present.

8 No sooner .... (*I have*) got home than the builders rang to say they couldn't come.

ENGLISH IN USE

Part 6, Discourse cloze

Read through the following text and then choose from the list (**A–J**) the phrase which best fits each of the spaces (**1–5**). Some of the suggested answers do not fit at all. The exercise begins with an example (**0**).

SOME AMAZING FACTS ABOUT LIGHTNING

Did you know that lightning travels up and down many times between the earth and the sky? It just looks as **(0)** ..J.. because it happens so fast. Travelling at the speed of light and carrying as much as one million volts, a stroke of lightning can do tremendous damage to buildings and often causes fires which lead to the destruction of thousands of trees. Lightning always seeks out the longest objects, especially if they are made of metal, so **(1)** .... , get rid of golf clubs, ice-axes and similar objects.

The next time you are caught in a thunderstorm, **(2)** .... , you should kneel on the ground with your feet close together and your hands on your knees. With luck, the lightning, **(3)** .... , will roll over your back and into the ground. It is better **(4)** .... but even being indoors may not protect you. In 1990, a family in a house in Lincolnshire, England were astonished when lightning came down their chimney, bounced off the fireplace across the living room and into the kitchen where it melted saucepans together and roasted instantaneously a leg of lamb they were going to have for dinner. They could have been killed **(5)** .... . Much more astonishing is the case of Edwin Robinson, a blind man struck by lightning and knocked unconscious. When he came to, he realised that he could see again.

A	if you are in the open during a thunderstorm
B	if you know what you are doing
C	if you can get to shelter
D	if you are not prepared
E	if they had been in the kitchen
F	if there is no shelter
G	if it hits you
H	if care isn't taken
I	if it hadn't been avoided
J	if it is going down

WRITING
Part 1, Leaflet and short note (CB page 178)

1 Read this writing task.

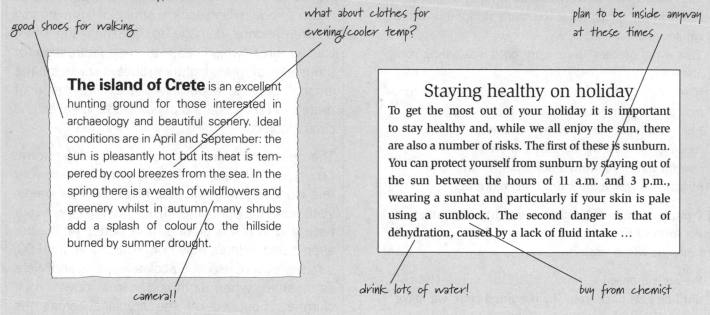

You are President of the Archaeology Society and you have planned a group expedition to the Greek island of Crete. You have decided to write a leaflet advising the members what to bring and warning them about any precautions they should take. Read the extract from a travel guide and the information sheet about the dangers of too much sun, to which you have added your own comments. Then, using the information carefully, write:

a) a leaflet for the society's members (approximately 200 words)

b) a short note to the former president asking him to check what you have written (approximately 50 words).

good shoes for walking

what about clothes for evening/cooler temp?

plan to be inside anyway at these times

The island of Crete is an excellent hunting ground for those interested in archaeology and beautiful scenery. Ideal conditions are in April and September: the sun is pleasantly hot but its heat is tempered by cool breezes from the sea. In the spring there is a wealth of wildflowers and greenery whilst in autumn many shrubs add a splash of colour to the hillside burned by summer drought.

Staying healthy on holiday
To get the most out of your holiday it is important to stay healthy and, while we all enjoy the sun, there are also a number of risks. The first of these is sunburn. You can protect yourself from sunburn by staying out of the sun between the hours of 11 a.m. and 3 p.m., wearing a sunhat and particularly if your skin is pale using a sunblock. The second danger is that of dehydration, caused by a lack of fluid intake …

camera!!

drink lots of water!

buy from chemist

2 Read the mark scheme for the task. This will tell you what the examiner is looking for in an ideal answer.

Content (points covered): leaflet – must mention all the points from the handwritten notes in the input. short note – should include a polite request for the former president to proofread the leaflet.

Organisation and cohesion: leaflet – could be divided into clear sections, e.g. items to bring and precautions (heat); could make use of short sentences and headings and/or bullet points to get points across effectively.

short note – may begin and end like a letter; the note is likely to consist of one paragraph only.

Range: leaflet – should use language suited to a leaflet i.e. listing points succinctly rather than complex sentences.

short note – the request should be phrased carefully (e.g. *I wondered if you'd mind* + *…ing*)

Register: leaflet and short note – both fairly informal. Both pieces of writing are for a very specific audience.

Target reader: leaflet – would have enough information to enable them to be well prepared for the trip.

short note – will agree to the request.

Accuracy: should not contain major errors that lead to misunderstandings or have a negative effect on the reader.

3 Now read this answer and do the questions below.

Visit to Crete

This leaflet has been written to help you make the most of your trip.

What to bring
When we set up each day you should have the following:
— A range of clothes for different weather temperatures
  e.g. light tops and shorts for the day, a cardigan for the
  evening when it is cooler
— Strong shoes as Crete can be hilly
— And of course, a camera with two roles of film! (The scenery is
  very beautiful.)
The group leader will carry a medical case for emergencies.

Protecting yourself
Although we will not be in Crete during the hottest season you can
still expect very warm temperatures. There are three main
precautions:
— Bring a big sunhat with a wide brim — the bigger the better!
— Bring a tube of suncreem from your chemist at home
— Carry a small beeker with a lid on for refilling with water. (You
  should drink at least 8 cups of water a day.)
You will see from the itinerary that we will be indoors during the
hottest period of the day — 11 a.m. to 3 p.m. — so don't worry
about the sun at these times.

by Sophie Max
President

Dear Simon

Here is the leaflet I plan to send to the group members before our trip. As you went to Crete the last time I wonder if you could have a look to it and tell me if there is anything else that needs to be added. Thank you in advance for doing this.

Regards

Sophie

---

1 a) Has the writer included all the essential information in the leaflet? Look at the handwritten notes in Exercise 1 and tick off those points that are covered in the leaflet. What extra information has the writer included that wasn't asked for but that would reassure the readers? Highlight it and put a tick (✓) next to it.

   b) Now read the short note. Does this answer do what the question asked for?

2 Has the writer organised the leaflet and the note appropriately? Use the advice on organisation to help you decide.

3 a) Underline the expression the writer uses to introduce the leaflet and put a tick (✓) next to it.

   b) Do the same in the note for an expression which can be used to thank somebody before they have done something for you.

4 Find the following errors and make the necessary corrections:

incorrect use of particle in a phrasal verb (leaflet)
incorrect use of a preposition (note)
spelling mistakes (leaflet)

4 Now write your own answer to the question.

Human behaviour

READING
Part 3, Gapped text

1 Read the following newspaper article. Six paragraphs have been removed. You must choose which of the paragraphs **A–G** match the numbered gaps **1–6**. There is one extra paragraph which does not fit in any of the gaps.

A spot of bother in the west wing ends as families resolve two-year squabble over country mansion

When university professor Jasper Rose retired, he abandoned the hothouse world of Cambridge for the secluded calm of a seventeenth century West Country mansion. There, for eight years, he and his wife whiled away their twilight years painting, playing the piano and entertaining friends in the west wing of the mansion.

1

The £10,000 civil action was brought by Dr Hampton, who accused art historian Professor Rose of behaving like a Lord of the Manor and parking his car on the gravel drive outside his neighbour's window. What started as a minor disagreement led to allegations involving a vandalised hedge, loud music and a vicious dog.

2

The judge had been told that 66-year-old Professor Rose retired to the west wing of Wingfield house ten years ago.

3

'One was not well. They had parked outside our front door. During lunch Dr Hampton rang us and spoke to my wife. As our guests left he came out and shouted at my wife. I cannot say that we have enjoyed good relations since then.'

4

On yet another occasion, he claimed, he was attacked by Dr Hampton's Alsatian. 'The dog was on the brink of being dangerous,' he said. 'It was bounding around and I turned my back. I felt a tongue, teeth and nose on my left hand. I said that if it did that again, I would have it put down.' One day, Mrs Rose, 67, parked her car in front of their front door only to find she had been boxed in by Dr Hampton's car.

5

'We had to move our bed to another room. It was unbearable. My sleeping pattern never really recovered.' Both sides refused to reveal details of the agreement, but it is believed that Professor Rose will in future leave his car on the drive only if it is 'reasonably necessary'.

6

Dr Hampton added, 'We are saddened that it came to court. We have settled with goodwill on both sides. We remain on good terms with our neighbours.' Mrs Rose said, 'I'm glad we stood up for our rights. If we had not, we would have been treated like tenants in our own home.'

A Professor Rose also claimed that Dr Hampton had cut back his beloved beech hedge, which stretched eighty metres along the drive, while he was on holiday. 'It has been a terrible devastation,' he said. 'I have become very friendly towards my hedge. I felt very strongly about it. When you look after trees, you begin to feel for them.'

B Afterwards, Dr Hampton, 39, who works in Bath, said, 'We want to sell the property but how can we sell when someone is effectively parking in our front garden. When he parked in front of our house, he blocked our view from the kitchen window. How would you like a car parked outside your house all the time?'

C Police, environmental health officers and the Royal Society for the Prevention of Cruelty to Animals were sucked into the row until yesterday, after two days of legal arguments, the two sides finally agreed a settlement. Peering over his spectacles, Judge John Weeks, who had refereed the dispute, sighed, 'I am glad you have eventually reached an agreement between yourselves.'

D 'Dr Hampton said he was going to leave his car there until Monday morning, so I called the police,' said Professor Rose. 'I also reported them to the environmental health people. Then that evening when we were going to bed, we heard continuous music from the room next to our bedroom. It wasn't very loud, but it was persistent. I tried to get some sleep but Dr Hampton's wife, Jacqueline, left the music on over the weekend.'

E Professor Rose said, 'I am astonished. I don't think that I am the Lord of the Manor and I do not behave in that way. It is not a manor house and I spent a lot of time in the USA. This is a very malicious accusation.'

F But their idyll was shattered when James Hampton, a doctor, moved into the unoccupied wing next door and claimed that the Roses' habitual parking spot was on his property. It began a two-year squabble over parking rights that ended with both men appearing before a judge in Bristol County Court.

G 'I moved there because it was out in the country and quite peaceful. We were pleased at first that the house next door was going to be occupied by a family. Children always smile and say amusing things – but they said some very rude things to me. Things deteriorated quite badly. We had two elderly ladies to lunch, both widows,' he said.

---

2 Complete each sentence with the correct particle. Most of these are from the text opposite but some are from the Coursebook.

1 The passengers on the train played a game of cards to *while* .... the time.

2 This food is cold. I'm going to *call* the waiter .... and complain.

3 The police have told Olivia that if her dog attacks another person it will have to be *put* .... immediately.

4 In spite of government laws many women still find themselves being *discriminated* .... in the workplace.

5 Can't you get rid of those old magazines? They're making a mess *piled* .... on the floor like that.

6 Kris doesn't like that jumper he bought recently. He's going to *take* it .... to the shop for a refund.

7 Sorry I'm late. Some idiot *boxed* my car .... by parking too close to mine.

8 People over sixty now *make* .... a sizeable number of the population.

9 When Brian's boss tried to dismiss him without good reason, everyone else in the office *stood* .... for him.

10 Penny kept quiet during the meal because she didn't want to be *sucked* .... a discussion about animal rights.

VOCABULARY

More informal expressions and phrasal verbs with *get* (CB page 166)

1 Rewrite the sentences below with a suitable expression using the verb *get*. Use a dictionary to help you, if necessary. The first has been done as an example.

1 Theatre tickets can be obtained in advance.
Look! I've managed to ....*get hold of*.............. some tickets for tomorrow's show.

2 Unpleasant though it may be to dismiss employees it is better if action is taken swiftly.
I know it's hard to sack someone but you need to .... as soon as possible.

3 Doctors usually advise us not to burden ourselves for long periods of time.
If you've got a problem you might find it helpful to ....

4 The annual gathering of managerial staff will take place during the Christmas holiday.
There's going to be the usual office .... in the Xmas holiday.

5 Although the crime was of a serious nature the judge showed leniency towards the accused.
The judge was soft and the burglar ....

6 Measures have been taken to prevent relatives benefiting from our client's death.
The old lady is making sure that none of her relatives .... her money.

7 There has been some delay with the submission of the report.
He .... finishing the report.

8 The lecture I attended was extremely technical and rather difficult to comprehend.
I .... the lecture this morning.

Choosing the right word

2 Complete the following sentences with the correct word from the box. There is one word you don't need.

> person people individual character
> mankind humanity

1 It is the responsibility of the .... to ensure that personal belongings are not left unattended.

2 I saw an odd-looking .... trying to break into your car a moment ago.

3 Modern technology is a great development for ....

4 The cost of a double room is £55 per .... per night.

5 Many world leaders are guilty of crimes against ....

> behaviour conduct manner
> demeanour way antics

6 Most places of work have a code of .... for their employees.

7 With her excellent telephone .... Tanya will make a really good receptionist.

8 The prisoner was released early due to good ....

9 I wish Adam wasn't always fooling around. His .... get a bit tiresome after a while.

10 Did you hear the president's latest speech? He's got a real .... with words.

Word formation (CB pages 182/183)

3 Complete these sentences with an appropriate word formed from the word in CAPITALS.

Tip: If you're required to form an adverb (usually from a noun or verb) it is usually helpful to form the adjective first and then the adverb.

1 Michelle .... announced that she was leaving her job and going to live abroad. COOL

2 The police found the .... car abandoned in a field. STEAL

3 Yolanda waved hello quite .... in spite of being depressed. CHEER

4 The boss of the company dealt .... with the employee caught stealing. COMPASSION

5 In his speech the politician suggested, somewhat .... , that all young people were criminals. CONTROVERSY

6 In many schools there are huge .... of fully trained and qualified teachers. SHORT

7 A number of workers suffering financial .... are unaware that help is available from the government. DIFFICULT

8 Before trying on that jumper you need to see the .... over there. ASSIST (compound word)

9 The police have been watching Clive for some time. He's under .... of fraud and forgery. SUSPECT

10 When Pat was found cheating in her exams she had to endure the .... of being excluded from college. HUMILIATE

ENGLISH IN USE
Part 4, Word formation

Read the texts below. Use the words in the box to form one word that fits in the same numbered space in the text. The exercise begins with an example (**0**).

ADDICTED TO COMPUTER GAMES

Tomorrow will see the (**0**) ...*publication*...... of a guide that will help parents find out if their child is suffering from computer game (**1**) .... The guide criticises many games for being (**2**) .... violent and explains that many experts believe they are affecting the (**3**) .... of our young children, leading them to the (**4**) .... that problems are best sorted out by fighting. The guide proposes that there should be a (**5**) .... scheme whereby every game would carry a sticker outlining its (**6**) .... for certain age groups. At present there are no such (**7**) ....

(0)	**PUBLISH**
(1)	ADDICT
(2)	EXCESS
(3)	BEHAVE
(4)	CONCLUDE
(5)	CERTIFY
(6)	SUIT
(7)	REQUIRE

DIET FEARS

Children today eat a diet 'too high in fat and too low in fibre', (**8**) .... claimed in a report yesterday. (**9**) .... show that two thirds eat no fruit or vegetables, although some are saying the survey was (**10**) .... Many other consumer surveys have shown a steady fall in fat (**11**) .... and a rise in Vitamin C (**12**) .... This paradox can partly be explained through class differences, with higher income groups spending (**13**) .... more on fruit and vegetables. The report argues eating habits formed during (**14**) .... are taken into adult life. The (**15**) .... of this is the need to instill healthy eating habits in our children.

(8)	NUTRITION
(9)	FIND
(10)	REPRESENT
(11)	CONSUME
(12)	TAKE
(13)	NOTICE
(14)	CHILD
(15)	CONSEQUENT

LANGUAGE REVIEW 2

<u>Underline</u> the correct form of the words in *italics* in the following sentences. Sometimes two answers are correct.

1 Terry *must have/must have been/can't have* got lost. He *should have/should be/should* arrived ages ago.

2 We *needn't have/didn't need to/needn't* come so early. There's no one here yet.

3 I *was able to/could/managed to* pass the exam even though I *couldn't/wasn't able to* finish all the questions.

4 I looked out of the window and realised that it *was raining/rained/had been raining*. But by the time I *was leaving/left/had been leaving* the house it *had stopped/stopped/was stopping*.

5 I *could/was allowed* to leave the exam room as I was feeling sick.

6 I *have to/must* remember to get my suit cleaned this weekend. I *have to/must* do a presentation at work.

7 I *haven't been watching/haven't watched/wasn't watching* any television this week and I *have read/have been reading/read* two books so far.

8 We *have been knowing/have known* each other now for almost 10 years.

9 They *have been winning/have won/won* three games so far this season.

10 That's the man *I was telling you about/whom I was telling you about/that I was telling you about him*.

11 Buckingham Palace, *where/which/that* had always been out of bounds to the general public, now generates a large income through tours of the building.

12 He passed his driving test despite *to take/he took/taking* virtually no driving lessons.

13 The weather was terrible on the holiday. *Nevertheless/Despite this/Although* we managed to get out quite a bit.

14 I regret *to tell/telling* you that we will not be renewing your contract.

15 I remembered *visiting/to visit/visit* my grandfather as a child. We used to go every Sunday. And he'd never forget *buy/to buy/buying* us a bar of chocolate each.

16 Alan suggested *to go/going/go* to see that film at the cinema this week.

17 After university he went on *becoming/to become/become* a leading figure in the Trade Union movement.

18 The teacher let the class *go/to go/going* early. He was later *seen/seeing/to see* going into a bar for a drink.

19 It's not worth *to go/going* by car. You'll never get a parking space and I can't stand *to drive/driving* round and round looking for somewhere.

20 We were told that the meeting *was to be held/was holding/was held* next week.

ENGLISH IN USE
Part 2, Structural cloze

Complete the following article by writing the correct word in each space. Use only one word for each space. The exercise begins with an example (**0**).

COACH FOR HIRE – TO SORT OUT YOUR LIFE!

(**0**) ......*Only*........ America, the land (**1**) .... exercise workouts and therapy, could come up (**2**) .... the idea of a life coach – a personal trainer to help you sort out your life. Somehow it's not surprising that these coaches have become (**3**) .... the rage there. Their popularity is spreading, however, across the Atlantic. We spoke to a client to find out how Life Coaching works and (**4**) .... it has changed her life. Montserrat Barons works three days a week for Spanish food importers. She (**5**) .... is Spanish but lives in London with her English husband and small daughter.

The problem: I'm finding work stressful, I've got no energy and (**6**) .... to admit to (**7**) .... irritable.

The coaching: A 40-minute telephone conversation which covered (**8**) .... from the state of my health to the state of my car.

The advice: I told my coach, Elizabeth, (**9**) .... I planned to write to the government about the lack of childcare. In Spain it's a woman's right but not (**10**) .... here. She understood but suggested I was wasting energy trying to run a campaign and that it (**11**) .... be better to find other mums in the same position and share childcare costs with them. She also suggested finding a local job to cut (**12**) .... the number of hours I spend commuting each week. (**13**) .... she asked me what I wanted to do with my life, I told her I dreamt of having my own business.

The results: The coaching (**14**) .... me realise how negative I'd been about my life. I'm keeping my eye open for a local job and I'm going to enrol on a tourism course. It's (**15**) .... if a great weight's been lifted from my shoulders. I was so impressed with Elizabeth that I'm going to carry on with her.

Answer key

UNIT 1 MAKING AN IMPRESSION

READING
Exercise 1
1 B, 2 A, 3/4 A/E, 5 B, 6 C, 7 E, 8 D, 9 A, 10 B, 11 A, 12 A
Exercise 2
1 close-knit community, 2 adored, 3 parents' evening, 4 trauma, 5 furious, 6 longed for, 7 waded in, 8 radical
Exercise 3
1 deeply, 2 serious, fine, 3 acceptable, 4 complete, 5 terrible

VOCABULARY
Exercise 1
1 attractive, 2 approachable, 3 outgoing, 4 chatty, 5 aggressive, 6 sociable, 7 bad-tempered, 8 well-groomed
Exercise 2
1 obsessive, 2 larger, 3 notorious, 4 familiar, 5 naive, 6 generous, 7 shrewd, 8 trusting
Exercise 3
1 G, 2 D, 3 E, 4 A, 5 C, 6 F, 7 H, 8 B
Exercise 4
1 owning up, 2 give in, hand in, 3 put ... forward, 4 get ... down, 5 choke back, 6 broken off, 7 telling ... off

ENGLISH IN USE
1 D, 2 C, 3 C, 4 A, 5 A, 6 B, 7 C, 8 A, 9 B, 10 C

LANGUAGE STUDY
Exercise 1
1 (L)
a) must have, b) won't, c) can't have
2 (O)
a) mustn't, b) don't have to, c) must
3 (N)
a) doesn't need to, b) needn't have
4 (P)
a) are not allowed to, b) was allowed to
5 (A)
a) couldn't/wasn't able to, b) was able to
Exercise 2
1 We *have to* tell
2 You *needn't have helped me/didn't need to help me*
3 You *don't need* the dictionary.
4 Were *you able to book*
5 I *have never been allowed* to
6 He *must have decided* to
7 I *needn't have worried* about
8 We *mustn't* proceed
9 I *won't be able to meet* you
10 That *can't be* John
Exercise 3
1 have never been to
2 have you known
3 haven't smoked
4 haven't finished my homework
5 I have eaten
6 he only been learning
7 hasn't been seen
8 haven't hired a car *since*
Exercise 4
1 have been trying, have you been, have been sitting, got back
2 Have you spoken, have tried, has been
3 have had, has never given, have been having/have had
4 have you two known, Didn't we meet
5 have you been doing, have been reading, have already read
6 have you done, have been using
7 have you been doing, dropped

8 have lived
9 have been living

ENGLISH IN USE
Exercise 1
1 *winds* me *up* (phrasal verb)
2 *Most* (quantifier), *have* (auxiliary verb), *because* (conjunction)
3 *in* (preposition), *the* (article)
4 *most* (comparative)
5 *It* (personal pronoun), *where* (relative pronoun)
Exercise 2
1 had, 2 he, 3 to, 4 the, 5 some, 6 with, 7 but, 8 more, 9 a, 10 were, 11 to, 12 then, 13 which

UNIT 2 GOING TOO FAR

READING
Exercise 1
1 B, 2 E, 3 C, 4 D, 5 C, 6 B, 7 D, 8 B, 9 A, 10 D, 11 B, 12 C
Exercise 2
2 typist, 3 supervisor, 4 musician, 5 employee, 6 newspaper reporter, 7 instructor, 8 trainee, 9 therapist, 10 historian
Exercise 3
1 into, 2 by, 3 to, 4 for, 5 in, 6 with, 7 at, 8 for

VOCABULARY
Exercise 1
exhilarated: thrilled, delighted
petrified: terrified, scared
challenged: tested, taxed
absorbed: enthralled, engrossed
inspired: motivated
delightful, scary
Exercise 2
1 terrified, 2 enthralling, 3 stimulating, 4 inspired, 5 delightful, 6 intrigued, 7 thrilling, 8 challenging
Exercise 3
1 absorbing/enthralling/engrossing, 2 inspired/motivated, 3 challenging/testing, 4 thrilled/delighted, 5 scary
Exercise 4
1 put, 2 stick, 3 push, 4 playing, 5 pose, 6 take, 7 tempting, 8 asking
Exercise 5
1 playing with fire, tempting fate, asking for trouble, push your luck
2 put people at risk, pose a threat
3 stick my neck out for you, take the plunge
Exercise 6
2 I, 3 A, 4 C, 5 H, 6 F, 7 B, 8 E, 9 D
Exercise 7
1 rambling, 2 pour, 3 polish, 4 tied, 5 carve, 6 revolves, 7 raking, 8 bordering

ENGLISH IN USE
Exercise 1
1 mountaineering, 2 risky, 3 enthusiasts, 4 tragic, 5 endurance, 6 heights, 7 activities, 8 unbelievable

LANGUAGE STUDY
Exercise 1
1 He met Susan, to whom he got married, in 1967.
2 She's the teacher for whom the students have a lot of respect.
3 We flew to Amsterdam, from where we caught our connecting flight.
4 South Africa is the country from which we get most of our gold.
5 That's the officer to whom I was speaking.
6 That's the point to which I was referring.
Exercise 2
Dear Sir or Madam
I am writing about the article 'The high-flyer' *that/which appeared in your newspaper recently.*

The journalist concerned, *who seemed supportive of these dangerous stunts*, fails to understand the most basic point. Professional stunt men do not take risks unnecessarily. They work under strictly controlled conditions *in which safety is of paramount importance*. This is completely different from Darren Newton's stunt *which was outlined in the article*. This was carried out at the Hilton Hotel, a very public place *where little was done to warn people of the stunt*. The journalist does not seem to realise such stunts endanger members of the public, *who may well be unaware of what is happening*. How would he feel if he were innocently walking down the road when someone tried out a similar stunt *that/which caused personal injury to her*?
I feel very strongly that newspapers like yours, *which have an enormous influence*, should show a more responsible attitude.
Yours faithfully
Exercise 3
1 got up, needed, 2 had been working, decided, 3 was crossing, came, hit, 4 opened, saw, 5 had finished, went, 6 were rushing, were getting
Exercise 4
1 had reached, 2 were preparing, 3 split up, 4 decided, 5 was/had been suffering, 6 went, 7 was looking, 8 walked, 9 was able to, 10 continued, 11 decided, 12 had arrived, 13 returned, 14 left, 15 had, 16 thought, 17 had gone, 18 presumed, 19 was staying, had stayed, 20 knew, 21 was missing, 22 had decided, 23 got, 24 went, 25 found, 26 flew

ENGLISH IN USE
Exercise 1
1 being, 2 ✓, 3 up, 4 ✓, 5 them, 6 so, 7 on, 8 whose, 9 ✓, 10 when, 11 ✓, 12 been, 13 ✓, 14 ✓, 15 had, 16 ✓

UNIT 3 GETTING TO THE TOP

READING
Exercise 2
1 B, 2 D, 3 A, 4 B, 5 D, 6 D
Exercise 3
1 (an) unexpected sight, 2 stimulating conversation, 3 a dinner party, 4 long-lost cousin, 5 (to) window-shop
Exercise 4
1 golden opportunity, 2 body of research, 3 concrete evidence, 4 missed opportunity, 5 current situation, 6 market research, 7 social situation, 8 solid evidence
Exercise 5
1 market research, 2 golden opportunity, 3 current situation, 4 concrete/solid evidence, 5 body of research, 6 social situation, 7 missed opportunity

VOCABULARY
Exercise 1
1 made it, 2 go according to plan, 3 make his mark, 4 making a go of, 5 rise to the top
Exercise 2

	has an object	is an idiom
get off (the ground)	✓	✓
get ahead		
pass over	✓	
get off (to a flying start)		✓
pull off	✓	
carry out	✓	
pay off		

Exercise 3
1 come up with, 2 paid off, 3 get ahead, 4 carry out, 5 got off to a flying start, 6 pull off, 7 get off the ground, 8 passed over
Exercise 4
1 of, 2 for, 3 on, 4 with, 5 on, 6 in, 7 on, 8 beyond

ENGLISH IN USE
Exercise 1
1 of, 2 up, 3 ✓, 4 such, 5 ✓, 6 ✓, 7 the, 8 off, 9 ✓, 10 in, 11 he, 12 on, 13 it, 14 ✓, 15 a, 16 ✓
Exercise 2
line 1, 2, 8, 10, 12
line 7, 15
line 11
line 13
line 4

LANGUAGE STUDY
Exercise 1
1 had learnt, 2 were, 3 had done, 4 had
Exercise 2
1 I wish/If only you lived closer.
2 I wish/If only I could read more often.
3 I wish/If only I had taken up his offer.
4 I wish/If only the film had been shorter.
5 I wish/If only the weather were better.
6 I wish/If only I hadn't eaten so much.
7 I wish/If only I hadn't overslept.
8 I wish/If only I had remembered (hadn't forgotten) to send Michael a birthday card.
Exercise 3
1 didn't, 2 wouldn't, 3 wouldn't, 4 didn't, 5 would, 6 didn't, 7 didn't, 8 would
Exercise 4
1 (will) get a headache.
2 ✓
3 (Unless you would have) If you hadn't told me, I'd
4 if I (had been) were you.
5 If it hadn't (have) been
6 They'll never win (provided) unless
7 ✓
8 we wouldn't (have been) be lost now.
Exercise 5
1 hadn't decided, wouldn't have met, wouldn't have been born, wouldn't be writing
2 had been, might/would have taken, had stayed, passed, might/would have
3 wouldn't be, hadn't broken, (hadn't) left
4 hadn't spent/didn't spend, would/might be
5 hadn't been stolen, wouldn't have asked, wouldn't have become, would/might not have decided, hadn't bought, wouldn't be driving

ENGLISH IN USE
Exercise 1
1 I, 2 E, 3 F, 4 G, 5 B, 6 H

UNIT 4 AMUSING YOURSELF
READING
Exercise 1
1 D, 2 A, 3 C, 4 D, 5 A, 6/7 C/D, 8/9 A/B, 10 D, 11 B, 12 A, 13 B
Exercise 2.1
1 episode
2 characters
3 programme-makers
4 plots
Exercise 2.2
1 programme-makers, 2 plot, 3 episode, 4 characters
Exercise 3
science fiction/fantasy/drama/series/cult show cover/edition/printing

VOCABULARY
Exercise 1
1 draughts, 2 draw, 3 browse, canvas, 4 disk, kilobytes, 5 board, 6 bass, band, 7 heroine, 8 Martial, 9 scene, 10 fêtes
Exercise 2
1 insecure, 2 infamous, 3 indifferent, 4 incapable, 5 inaudible, 6 thoughtless, 7 powerless, 8 countless, 9 ageless, 10 harmless
Exercise 3
Sentences 8, 9 and 10 are not negative in meaning.
Exercise 4
1 keep, 2 to, 3 dissolved, 4 about, 5 raised, 6 head, 7 giggles, 8 at

ENGLISH IN USE
Exercise 1
1 collection, 2 explanation, 3 production, 4 delivery, 5 disappearance, 6 developments, 7 misconception, 8 investment
Exercise 2
1 patterned, 2 sentimental, 3 timeless, 4 dangerous, undercooked, 5 considerable, 6 beneficial, 7 attentive, 8 untimely
Exercise 3
1 discovery, 2 laughter, 3 irritation, 4 humorous, 5 uninhabited, 6 priceless, 7 speech, 8 boredom, 9 uninteresting, 10 entertainment, 11 performance, 12 reductions, 13 traditional, 14 variety, 15 reasonable

LANGUAGE STUDY
Exercise 1
1 guilty about forgetting
2 is no chance of you winning
3 has a reputation for losing
4 no substitute for eating
5 believe in making
6 concentrated on answering
7 is obsessed with checking
8 protested about having
Exercise 2
1 to examine, 2 talking, 3 making, 4 singing, 5 to behave, 6 to buy, 7 to indicate, 8 to take
Exercise 3
1 being, 2 telling, 3 putting off, 4 to follow, 5 not getting, 6 going, 7 being, 8 not having, 9 to make, 10 seeing
Exercise 4
1 a little, 2 little, 3 rather, 4 fairly, 5 virtually, 6 extremely, 7 indeed, 8 quite

ENGLISH IN USE
Exercise 1
1 1 I'm going to visit John in London in May.
2 The Principal will be meeting some Russian visitors on Monday morning.
2 1 Tomorrow should turn out fine. However, cold winds are expected from the North.
2 You could go on a diet. Alternatively, have you thought about taking up exercise?
3 1 Although the weather was bad, we had a great time.
2 This is Sarah, who started with us yesterday.
3 His contract, which runs out soon, is not expected to be renewed.
4 We're going to Italy, Spain and then China, if we can get a visa that is.
4 1 'Andrea,' Terry said. 'Have you seen my umbrella?'
2 'Anyway, we'd better be leaving,' said Karen. 'It's getting late.'
5 1 Steve's borrowing his dad's car for the weekend.
2 During the 1960s he led many of the students' demonstrations.

6 1 I bumped into my ex-boyfriend last Saturday in the car park.
2 She's got a beautiful three-year-old daughter.
Exercise 2
1 it's, 2 ✓, 3 them?, 4 unusable, so, 5 ✓, 6 firework, 7 ✓, 8 handle, which, 9 off, 10 ✓, 11 to, 12 forgotten, 13 scene, 14 beautifully, 15 quite, 16 ✓

UNIT 5 CREATIVITY
READING
Exercise 1
1 D, 2 C, 3 D, 4 B, 5 D, 6 A
Exercise 2
1 to, 2 of, 3 out, 4 by, 5 out, 6 out, 7 as, 8 for
Exercise 3
1 in, 2 against, 3 on, 4 on, 5 on, 6 on, 7 in, 8 by, 9 to, 10 on, 11 of, 12 for/about, 13 with, 14 of

VOCABULARY
Exercise 1
1 dramatically, 2 electrifying, 3 independence, 4 poetic, 5 critical, 6 orderliness, 7 musician, 8 narrative
Exercise 2
1 grew, 2 iron, 3 fizzled, 4 poured, 5 held, 6 break, 7 washed, 8 run
Exercise 3
1 set up, 2 settled down, 3 put out, 4 falling apart, 5 got over
Exercise 4
1 fell apart, 2 set up, 3 settled down, 4 getting over, 5 put out

ENGLISH IN USE
Exercise 1
1 C, 2 B, 3 D, 4 D, 5 B, 6 A, 7 C, 8 D, 9 C, 10 A, 11 B, 12 D, 13 A, 14 D, 15 B

LANGUAGE STUDY
Exercise 1
1 like, 2 as, 3 as, 4 eating, 5 used to smoke, 6 is supposed, 7 suppose, 8 winning
Exercise 2
1 used to, 2 used to, 3 would, 4 would, 5 used to, 6 didn't use to
Exercise 3
1 ✓, 2 After I had washed the car ..., 3 because I felt tired ..., 4 ✓, 5 When I entered the room ..., 6 ✓, 7 ✓, 8 ... which made me really mad!
Exercise 4
1 Being bad at ... the Inspector,
2 Meeting her ..., 3 ... making him feel,
4 Learning ..., 5 ... showing no emotion ...

ENGLISH IN USE
Exercise 2
1 were, 2 worth, 3 There, 4 in, 5 with, 6 as, 7 even, 8 far, 9 who, 10 if/though, 11 out, 12 following/after, 13 at, 14 no, 15 those, 16 just

UNIT 6 COMMITMENTS
READING
Exercise 1
1 C, 2 H, 3 F, 4 A, 5 D, 6 B, 7 G
Exercise 2
1 fad, 2 reticent, 3 in unison, 4 sent off, 5 gaudy, 6 ligament, 7 showing off, 8 turf

VOCABULARY
Exercise 1
1 into, 2 as, 3 to, 4 with, 5 to, 6 on, 7 in, 8 into, 9 on, 10 to
Exercise 2
1 H, 2 B, 3 E, 4 D, 5 G, 6 A, 7 C, 8 I, 9 F
Exercise 3

1 get together, 2 cheating on, depend on, split up, 3 hold down, piles up, 4 stick to, 5 let (me) down, Keep up

Exercise 4
1 obligation, 2 requirement, 3 duty, 4 commitment, 5 responsibility, 6 word, 7 oath, 8 guarantee, 9 promise, 10 vow

ENGLISH IN USE
Exercise 1
1 practice, 2 situation, 3 sedatives, 4 replacement, 5 crossings, 6 leadership, 7 imaginative, 8 reductions, 9 notoriety, 10 creativity

Exercise 2
1 coloured, 2 delightful, 3 impossibly, 4 disadvantaged, 5 unofficially, 6 unacceptable, 7 irreplaceable, 8 illegible, 9 artistic, 10 indefinitely

Exercise 3
1 promotion, 2 representative, 3 responsibility, 4 anxiety, 5 unenthusiastic, 6 advice, 7 appointment, 8 buildings, 9 locations, 10 relatives, 11 travellers, 12 disabled, 13 unfortunately, 14 commitment, 15 safety

LANGUAGE STUDY
Exercise 1
1 The Police are warning drivers *to drive* carefully … . They are suggesting *staying* (*that people stay*) at home … .
2 … I suggest you *speak* to your new teacher … .
3 The Government inspectors are advising *people* not to eat … . They also warn *about cooking* (*warn us to cook/warn that we should cook*) chicken … .
4 We *recommend that you* don't surf the Internet … .

Exercise 2
1 suggestion, 2 warning, 3 recommendations, 4 advice

Exercise 3
1 He suggested servicing the car.
2 She warned him to hand the work in on time.
3 The Government has recommended that people stop smoking.
4 She advised him to save the letter to floppy disk.

Exercise 4
1 In spite of not being picked for the team he wasn't disappointed.
2 No matter how much he begs me, I'm not working late tonight.
3 Despite being hit by a lot of injuries the team have been playing well.
4 You may have got 80 per cent for your last test but you still need to do some practice.
5 However much I study phrasal verbs I can't understand them.
6 In spite of (me) telling him to arrive 30 minutes before the test he was still late.
7 Even if he apologises I'm still not speaking to him.
8 Even though he saw a few things he liked he didn't buy anything.

ENGLISH IN USE
Exercise 1
1 E, 2 F, 3 C, 4 B, 5 D, 6 A

Exercise 3
1 I, 2 G, 3 C, 4 D, 5 B, 6 F

Exercise 4
Gap 1 Link word = Although. Antonym = tolerant x irritated.
Gap 2 Link word = Although. Different expression = listen to my wife's point of view x Agree.
Gap 3 Link word = so. Pronoun = that.

Gap 4 Link word = but. Pronoun = one.
Gap 5 Antonym = take each other for granted x show appreciation. Link word = Although.
Gap 6 statement = I don't think our marriage has changed. An example = we're the same sort of people … .

UNIT 7 HOME SWEET HOME
READING
Exercise 1
1 A, 2 B, 3 B, 4 A, 5 C, 6 D, 7 C

Exercise 2
1 social services
2 low income
3 virtually unaltered
4 confectionery bars
5 local dialect
6 chemical fertilisers
7 promising career

Exercise 3
1 local dialect, 2 confectionery bars, 3 low income, 4 chemical fertilisers, 5 promising career, 6 virtually unaltered

VOCABULARY
Exercise 1
1 to, 2 In, of, 3 at, 4 in, 5 to, 6 In, of, 7 on, 8 for, 9 by, 10 on

Exercise 2
proud: prided, house-proud, pride
home: homely, homeless, homegrown, homesick, homeward
clean: cleaner, clean-up, cleanliness, cleanse

Exercise 3
1 prided, 2 house-proud, 3 pride, 4 homely, 5 homeless, 6 homegrown, 7 homesick, 8 homeward, 9 cleaner, 10 clean-up, 11 cleanliness, 12 cleanse

ENGLISH IN USE
Exercise 1
1 F, 2 E, 3 G, 4 A, 5 H, 6 C, 7 D, 8 B

Exercise 2
1 seeing eye to eye, 2 was given the sack, 3 looking into, 4 has fallen out with, 5 doing away with, 6 put up with, 7 hasn't come up to scratch, 8 hold your tongue

Exercise 3
1 survey/thorough inspection, 2 behalf, 3 attention/repair, 4 expensive, 5 abandoned, 6 necessary/essential, 7 lack of/absence of, 8 destroyed/missing, 9 valuable/of value, 10 According to, 11 little/no progress/no effort, 12 to reconsider, 13 reduced

LANGUAGE STUDY
Exercise 1
1 arrive/are arriving, is going to phone/is phoning, will be taking/is going to take, will be sitting/are going to be sitting
2 will have to/are going to have to, will have finished/will finish, are coming/will be coming
3 are going to buy/are buying, am going to book/am booking, are going to be/will be

Exercise 2
1 I'm seeing the doctor at 3.00.
2 We're planning to move into a bigger house next year.
3 The course starts on May 13th.
4 The roadworks will have been completed before the busy summer period.
5 I'll do that for you.
6 … I'm going to be sick.
7 I'll be meeting the Director at that time.
8 I think they'll win, as long as the crowd get behind them.

Exercise 3
1 Once he has had dinner, I'll tell him the bad news.
2 When we go to Paris we'll be staying with relations.
3 I think I'll be good enough to pass by the time I do the exam.
4 I won't be able to lend you any money until I get paid on Friday.
5 As soon as I've finished working on the car I'll take you into town.
6 Will you wait for the phone call while I go shopping?
7 Provided you can show proof of purchase we will exchange the goods.
8 If the Government raise interest rates, small businesses are going to be in trouble.

Exercise 4
1 arrive/are arriving, 2 get, 3 will give, 4 am staying/am going to stay, 5 am going to be/will be, 6 meet, 7 will have completed, 8 will be able to, 9 will call, 10 have written, 11 will phone, 12 am looking, 13 will finish, 14 will be laughing

ENGLISH IN USE
Exercise 1
1 The Prime Minister, who is visiting the Middle East, warned against strike action.
2 Look at that bird. I think its wing is injured.
3 They've got a three-year-old daughter.
4 Have you got any plans for New Year's Eve?
5 Can you get me some sugar, a tin of soup and a loaf of bread?
6 'We have every officer available working on the case,' the chief constable said.
7 Always look carefully for punctuation errors in sentences.
8 Actually, I think we had better be leaving now.

Exercise 2
1 film, in, 2 ✓, 3 performance, 4 'I, 5 ✓, 6 immediately, 7 Gaunt, 52, 8 friends, 9 ✓, 10 don't, 11 ✓, 12 appropriate, 13 ✓, 14 ceiling, 15 Gaunt's, 16 daughter

UNIT 8 HONESTY, THE BEST POLICY
READING
Exercise 1
1 C, 2 D, 3 B, 4 C, 5 A, 6 A

Exercise 2
1 get, 2 jump, 3 picking, 4 read, 5 snatched, 6 vandalised, 7 take, 8 sent

VOCABULARY
Exercise 1
1 J, 2 D, 3 C, 4 A, 5 F, 6 E, 7 H, 8 G, 9 B, 10 I

Exercise 2
2 rip-off, 3 layout, 4 handouts, 5 incoming, 6 outcry, 7 climb-down, 8 blackouts, 9 worn out, 10 drop-in

Exercise 3
1 down, 2 off, 3 in, 4 down, 5 up, 6 down, 7 in, 8 in, 9 out

ENGLISH IN USE
Exercise 1
1 scene, 2 qualms, 3 recompense, 4 posed, 5 turn, 6 reported, 7 remorse, 8 risk, 9 valuables, 10 put

Exercise 2
1 A, 2 B, 3 B, 4 D, 5 C, 6 D, 7 A, 8 B, 9 A, 10 D, 11 A, 12 C, 13 B, 14 B, 15 A

LANGUAGE STUDY
Exercise 1
2 point out, 3 insist, 4 remind, 5 admit, 6 complain, 7 warn, 8 conclude

Exercise 2

1 He explained that sales had been extremely poor over the previous few months …

2 … pointed out that overseas investors had refused to continue offering financial assistance.

3 He insisted the company had no intention of making any staff redundant at that stage.

4 He reminded everyone that the company still had orders to keep them going until well into the beginning of the following year.

5 He admitted that if the situation didn't improve soon the company may have to look at its staffing levels.

6 He complained that the Government weren't giving the company the assistance they needed.

7 He warned everyone that if interest rates continued the situation was going to get worse.

8 He concluded by saying that everyone needed to be prepared for some difficult times ahead.

Exercise 3

1 He offered to do the washing up.

2 He advised her to try the new supermarket on the main street.

3 She suggested seeing a doctor about her cough.

4 I don't believe in making people do military service.

5 She insisted that the Government would not give in to terrorist demands.

6 He ordered him to get out of the car and to empty his pockets.

7 She admitted driving/that she had been driving a little too fast.

8 He agreed to get it done by the following day.

9 He denied having borrowed/borrowing the pen.

10 He objected to working that weekend.

Exercise 4

The policeman gave her directions.

The jacket cost her a fortune.

The guide showed her the exhibits/the exhibits to her.

Customs refused him a visa.

The bank lent her money/lent money to her.

The DJ played him a record/played a record for him.

The tailor made him a suit/made a suit for him.

The boss offered her promotion/promotion to her.

Exercise 5

1 Could you suggest a good film?

2 Can you explain (to me) how this works?

3 'You lent it to him.'

4 Can you send them to them?

5 Can I get you a drink?

6 Who shall we send them to?

7 I wrote my friend a letter.

8 Could you give that magazine to me/Could you give me that magazine for a moment?

9 I bought a bunch of flowers for my mum.

10 Our car causes us so many problems.

ENGLISH IN USE

Exercise 1

1 auxiliary – have

2 determiner – a

3 preposition – in

4 conjunction – Although

5 pronoun – me

6 relative – that/which

Exercise 2

1 quite, 2 hardly, 3 just, 4 over, 5 far, 6 still, 7 well, 8 even

Exercise 3

1 how, 2 himself, 3 without, 4 which, 5 also, 6 will/may, 7 only, 8 same, 9 into/to, 10 far, 11 it, 12 after, 13 were, 14 one, 15 other

UNIT 9 MAKING A LIVING
READING

Exercise 1

1 D, 2 C, 3 F, 4 A, 5 B, 6 E

Exercise 2

1 unsatisfactory, 2 underqualified, 3 unregulated, 4 helplessness, 5 uncontrollable, 6 magical, 7 achievement, 8 unfashionable

Exercise 3

1 disease, 2 susceptible, 3 succumb, 4 ✓, 5 achieve, 6 ✓, 7 questioned, 8 investigators

VOCABULARY

Exercise 1

overtime, part-time, computer literate, one-man, well-known, handmade, self-employed, traditional-style, over-anxious, long-term

Exercise 2

1 computer literate, 2 well-known, 3 traditional-style, 4 over-anxious, 5 long-term, 6 overtime, 7 self-employed, 8 handmade, 9 one-man, 10 part-time

Exercise 3

1 in, 2 towards, 3 in, 4 under, 5 to, 6 to, 7 in, 8 for, 9 for, 10 of, 11 in, 12 up, 13 to, 14 out, 15 in, 16 on

Exercise 5

1 drifting, 2 aspires, 3 stamp, 4 chew, 5 thrives, 6 beavering, 7 ranks, 8 sucking

ENGLISH IN USE

Exercise 1

2 given the impression, 3 come to any agreement, 4 give their opinions, 5 meet our requirements, 6 take into consideration, 7 making an appearance, 8 near completion

Exercise 2

1 interested in/keen on, 2 forthcoming, 3 decisions have, 4 maximum of, 5 preference, 6 previous occasion, 7 writing, 8 within ten 9 their/the fees/expenses, 10 refund, 11 their return/returning, 12 receipts, 13 required/obliged

LANGUAGE STUDY

Exercise 1

1 The moment I went out it started to rain.

2 In addition to winning the 100 metres, he came second in the long jump.

3 The company has expanded in East Asia. Moreover, it has consolidated its position in Europe.

4 He passed his exam even though he didn't do any work.

5 The car hasn't been going very well. Nevertheless, I think we should still try the journey.

6 There has been talk that the President is unwell. On the contrary, he has never been fitter.

7 Since they hadn't had a holiday for a few years, they decided to go abroad.

8 Despite having two players sent off, they won 3–0.

9 In spite of the fact that the house had locks on all doors and windows the burglar still got in.

10 While we admit to being slow to respond to your letter, we have done all we can.

11 The bodywork is in terrible condition whereas the engine's as good as new.

12 Sally's doing really well at school. In contrast, Jamie doesn't seem to like it at all.

13 Although I've been taking the medicine, I don't feel all that good.

14 As you've all worked extremely hard today, have an early day.

Exercise 2

1 Steve has been working at the company for almost 15 years and his work record is excellent despite suffering from several illnesses over the past year.

2 He has continued to be one of the most popular members of the team. Moreover, he contributes immensely to staff morale.

3 Colleagues have been willing to help with his work during periods of illness because he is very popular

4 Unfortunately, there hasn't been any sign of improvement. On the contrary, he has seemed to get worse in the past month.

5 Although colleagues have been keen to help out in the past, they are no longer able to deal efficiently with the extra work involved.

6 I appreciate that the company has not been employing new staff recently. Nevertheless, I feel we need to appoint a part-time clerical worker to cover for Mike and allow him the chance to take extended leave.

7 This will hopefully enable him to fully recover, whereas if he struggles on in his present condition, the situation is unlikely to improve.

8 Steve is a valued member of staff. Therefore, I strongly recommend we employ someone part-time.

ENGLISH IN USE

Exercise 1

1 he – pronoun, 2 so – conjunction, 3 in – preposition, 4 been – participle, 5 enough – adverb, 6 The – determiner, 7 more – adverb, 8 yet – conjunction, 9 have – auxiliary verb, 10 it – pronoun, 11 on – preposition, 12 so – adverb

Exercise 2

1 by, 2 as, 3 are, 4 the, 5 ✓, 6 also, 7 every, 8 they, 9 to, 10 ✓, 11 in, 12 for, 13 ✓, 14 ✓, 15 up, 16 be

Exercise 3

Pronouns, determiners, conjunctions, prepositions, adverbs.

UNIT 10 JUST DESERTS
READING

Exercise 1

1 D, 2 G, 3 A, 4 E, 5 C, 6 B

Exercise 2

1 F, 2 A, 3 D, 4 E, 5 B, 6 H, 7 C, 8 G

Exercise 3

1 still really scared, 2 an initial reluctance, 3 endured the humiliation of, 4 It dawned on me, 5 boring voice, 6 consequences of his actions, 7 the perfect certainty, 8 told

VOCABULARY

Exercise 1

1 down, 2 out, 3 on, of, 4 off, about, 5 of, to, in, 6 of, 7 out, 8 by/with, 9 to, 10 by

Exercise 2

1 a penalty, b penalties, 2 sentence, 3 criminal, 4 punishment, 5 law, 6 rap, 7 make

Exercise 3

1 unarmed, 2 conflicting, 3 reformed, 4 worked, 5 undisturbed, 6 continued, 7 practising, 8 accusing, 9 embarrassing, 10 established

ENGLISH IN USE

Exercise 1

1 intensive, 2 advisable, 3 irresistible, 4 unkindly, 5 broken

Exercise 3

1 stolen, 2 spokesman, 3 respectable, 4 thefts, 5 shoplifter, 6 consideration, 7 warning, 8 effective, 9 indication, 10 improvements,

11 inspectors, 12 advice, 13 obligation, 14 products, 15 unlikely

LANGUAGE STUDY
Exercise 1
1 be posted, 2 have been posted, 3 to be intimidated, 4 being taken, 5 to be found
Exercise 2
1 I'm afraid (that) 300 people will have to be made redundant.
2 The robbers were seen escaping in a blue BMW.
3 The defendant was allowed to sit during questioning.
4 Rooms should be vacated by 12.00 a.m.
5 Lunch is served in the conference centre.
6 You will be informed of the changes by the bank as soon as possible.
7 He was relieved not to be called up for military service.
8 Drivers may be made to pay more for petrol by the government.
Exercise 3
1 It has often been said that money doesn't bring happiness.
2 It is feared that as many as 3,000 people have lost their homes in the flood.
3 It is argued that people are eating far too much salt in their diet.
4 It has been suggested that the soap opera should be rescheduled
Exercise 4
1 The people elected to do the job did really well.
2 The woman rescued from the fire is recovering in hospital.
3 The parents invited to the party were asked to bring some food.
4 The director awarded the prize was overcome with emotion.
Exercise 5 (Suggested answers)
1 A middle-aged man, arrested yesterday for armed robbery, has escaped from police custody today. The man, last seen driving off in a stolen Fiat, is described as extremely dangerous.
2 A beach in the North West, often used by local children, has been found to be contaminated due to high levels of radioactive waste. It has been closed by the local council. Samples of soil taken by inspectors have been examined and appear to contain twice the acceptable level of radiation.

ENGLISH IN USE
Exercise 1
1 D, 2 E, 3 H, 4 G, 5 A, 6 C, 7 F, 8 B
Exercise 2
1 I, 2 D, 3 E, 4 C, 5 F, 6 H

UNIT 11 A SENSE OF BELONGING
READING
Exercise 1
1 B, 2/3 A/D, 4 E, 5/6 B/D, 7 C, 8 D, 9/10 A/E, 11 A, 12 D, 13 C, 14 D, 15 C, 16 D, 17 A, 18 B, 19 B, 20 D, 21 A
Exercise 2
1 realistic, 2 enraptured, 3 idyllic, 4 windswept, 5 modernisation, 6 resourceful, 7 inhabitants, 8 enterprising

VOCABULARY
Exercise 1
1 through, 2 up, 3 up, 4 up, 5 off, 6 out, 7 along, 8 away, 9 away 10 in
Exercise 2
1 E, 2 B, 3 A, 4 B, 5 G, 6 D, 7 C, 8 F

Exercise 3
1 lodge, 2 farms, 3 council house, 4 trailer, 5 mansion, 6 housing estate, 7 shack/hut
Exercise 4
1 in, 2 beyond, 3 on, 4 in, 5 for, 6 in, of, 7 as, 8 at, of, 9 of, 10 in

ENGLISH IN USE
Exercise 1
1 emigrate, 2 thriving, 3 bleached, 4 trend, 5 taking, 6 cry, 7 building
Exercise 2
1 A, 2 B, 3 D, 4 C, 5 A, 6 B, 7 A, 8 B, 9 A, 10 C, 11 A, 12 B, 13 D, 14 B, 15 C
Exercise 3
There are examples of each type of word.

LANGUAGE STUDY
Exercise 1
1 What, 2 is, 3 It, 4 where, 5 that, 6 when, 7 What, 8 is
Exercise 2
1 Going out to restaurants is what I really enjoy.
2 What really upsets me is people who don't put the top back on the toothpaste.
3 It is Brazil that have won the World Cup the most times, not Italy
4 People who push in front of me in a queue make/get me so angry
5 What you haven't done is pay me back that money you owe me.
6 It is June when the exam takes place, not July.
7 What I don't like is having to do all the housework on my own.
8 Going to work during the dark winter mornings is what makes me fed up.
Exercise 3 (Suggested answers)
'… What the leader of the Opposition fails to understand is that more people are getting treated in our hospitals under this Government. It is this Government that is determined to increase the educational opportunities of the people of this country. What concerns this Government are the people who have little. It was the Opposition party that spent years ignoring the needs of the people, not us. We appreciate the needs of the people. What we don't do is treat them with disrespect. It was the Prime Minister who was the person who vowed to reduce unemployment. It was this Government that has been successful in this endeavour. What concerns the Government is the health and prosperity of our nation.'

ENGLISH IN USE
Exercise 1
1 B, 2 C, 3 D, 4 H, 5 A, 6 F, 7 G, 8 E
Exercise 2
1 not/hardly/little, 2 other, 3 When/If, 4 be, 5 so, 6 ever, 7 the, 8 only, 9 which, 10 with, 11 it, 12 why/how, 13 as, 14 although/but, 15 in

UNIT 12 CALAMITIES AND MISHAPS
READING
Exercise 1
1 F, 2 A, 3 C, 4 B, 5 E, 6 D
Exercise 2
1 prudent, 2 wry, 3 fundamental, 4 saps, 5 savage , 6 terrain, 7 preach, 8 fatalities

VOCABULARY
Exercise 1
1 taken, covered, 2 pulled, protect, 3 rounded, hand, 4 taken, 5 pulled, 6 handed, 7 turn, 8 round, 9 turn, 10 turned

Exercise 2
1 against/about, 2 in, 3 to, 4 on, 5 in, at, of, 6 in, at, 7 by, 8 by, 9 from, 10 on, 11 in, 12 in
Exercise 3
1 pitch/put up, 2 made, 3 deposit/leave, 4 carrying out/conducting, 5 had/suffered, 6 makes, 7 shudder, 8 participate/take part, 9 acting/posing, 10 made
Exercise 4
1 hazard, 2 services, 3 ordeal, 4 fix, 5 warning, 6 incident, 7 accident, 8 nightmare

ENGLISH IN USE
1 B, 2 C, 3 D, 4 D, 5 A, 6 C, 7 B, 8 D, 9 B, 10 C, 11 D, 12 A, 13 C, 14 B, 15 B

LANGUAGE STUDY
Exercise 1
1 I won't call you unless I hear something.
2 You can't drive a car if you're not 17.
3 Guests are allowed to use the washing facilities on condition that the room is locked up when finished.
4 You can borrow the car as long as you get it back before 8.00.
5 The Government will only discuss the issue if there are no preconditions.
6 You can get into that club provided you wear a jacket and tie.
Exercise 2
1 By the way
2 or something like that
3 By and large
4 To cut a long story short
5 Well
6 In fact
Exercise 3
1 In fact, 2 or something like that, 3 and that was that, 4 To cut a long story short/Anyway, 5 As I said, 6 To cut a long story short/Anyway/Well, 7 Anyway/Well
Exercise 4
1 Never have I witnessed such behaviour.
2 Had the union not been present at the meeting we would have all been made redundant.
3 Had we known of their plans earlier we could have organised some form of resistance.
4 Not until our demands have been met will we be satisfied.
5 On no account must we give in to their heavy-handed tactics.
6 Only when the management agree to drop their proposals will we withdraw our threat of strike action.

ENGLISH IN USE
Exercise 1
1 weight, 2 . But, 3 Arctic, 4 ✓, 5 Antarctica's, 6 ✓, 7 thick – eighty, 8 tomorrow, 9 current, 10 centimetres, 11 cause, 12 fact, as, 13 models suggest, 14 thicker., 15 Pole, 16 sea-levels
Exercise 2
Capitals, homophones, full stops, apostrophes, natural pauses, hyphens, i before e, double consonants.

UNIT 13 THE NATURAL WORLD
READING
Exercise 1
1 B, 2/3 B/C, 4 F, 5 C, 6 F, 7 E, 8 A, 9 F, 10 E, 11 A, 12 D, 13 D, 14 C, 15 B, 16 F, 17 A, 18 E
Exercise 2
1 swarm, 2 stung, 3 bite, 4 camouflage, 5 flicking, 6 squirting, 7 venomous

VOCABULARY
Exercise 1
1 signs, 2 breeding, 3 extinction, 4 borrowed,
5 natural, 6 species, 7 glimpse, 8 inhabited
Exercise 2
1 to, 2 at, 3 within, 4 from, 5 for, 6 by, 7 on,
8 from, 9 on, 10 in
Exercise 4
1 end up, 2 curl up, 3 thrown away, 4 wrap up,
5 given up, 6 died down, 7 set off, 8 plunged
into, 9 tired out, 10 set up, gone through

ENGLISH IN USE
Exercise 1
1 think, 2 least damage, 3 need, 4 cut down,
5 Every week, 6 don't take/don't collect, 7 rid
of, 8 buy, 9 unless, 10 take, 11 a local, 12 good
for, 13 doesn't need/use/have

LANGUAGE STUDY
Exercise 1
1 Having had, 2 Putting, 3 Having bet,
4 believing, 5 Having, 6 Having been arrested,
7 Realising, 8 having been concerned
Exercise 2
1 Having fixed the car, he went to work.
2 Feeling a little sick, she decided to go to bed.
3 Having washed the dishes, he sat down to
watch TV/After washing...
4 Knowing that the traffic was going to be
heavy, he left early for work.
5 Having agreed to do the job cheaply, he could
hardly now refuse.
6 Being the youngest child, Clare often gets her
own way more.
7 Having finished the exam, the candidate
admitted he had cheated.
8 The weather not being very good, they
decided to stay at home.
Exercise 3
1 Arrested for the recent post office robbery,
James is expected to be charged today.
2 Held every four years, the Olympic Games is
arguably one of the world's biggest sporting
competitions.
3 Thinking that the teacher was going to be off
sick, the students in Group B stayed at home.
4 Having been sold a defective machine, I
demand a refund.
5 Believed to date back millions of years, the
fossil is supposed to be one of the largest ever
found.
6 Painted by the artist early in his career, the
landscape shows a remarkable sense of
proportion.
7 Realising/Having realised that the course was
of no interest to her at all, she decided to drop
out of university.
8 Having been written in the 12th century, the
manuscripts were expected to fetch more than
£1 million in the auction.
Exercise 4
Aiming to fulfil
Having always been fascinated
Having joined Vicki
Sounds emitted
taking us about six miles out
We watched them surfacing and diving,
(suggested answer)
Known by Vicki since birth,
Swimming around and around, sometimes back
and forth right underneath the boat, the dolphin
got close enough to us to touch. (suggested
answer)

LANGUAGE REVIEW 1
Exercise 1
1 have to, 2 used to, used to/would, 3 have
been doing, have had, have had, 4 which,
5 who, 6 whom, 7 had finished, 8 forgot
Exercise 2
1 to wait, 2 to eat/eating, 3 to see, 4 wouldn't
argue, 5 would call, 6 being, 7 is said, 8 had I

ENGLISH IN USE
1 A, 2 F, 3 G, 4 C, 5 E

UNIT 14 HUMAN BEHAVIOUR
READING
Exercise 1
1 F, 2 C, 3 G, 4 A, 5 D, 6 B
Exercise 2
1 away, 2 over, 3 down, 4 against, 5 up, 6 back,
7 in, 8 up, 9 up, 10 into

VOCABULARY
Exercise 1
1 get hold of, 2 get it over and done with, 3 get
it off your chest, 4 get together, 5 got off lightly,
6 get their hands on, 7 hasn't got round to,
8 didn't get anything out of
Exercise 2
1 individual, 2 character, 3 mankind, 4 person,
5 humanity, 6 conduct, 7 manner, 8, behaviour,
9 antics, 10 way
Exercise 3
1 coolly, 2 stolen, 3 cheerfully,
4 compassionately, 5 controversially,
6 shortages, 7 difficulties, 8 shop-assistant,
9 suspicion, 10 humiliation

ENGLISH IN USE
1 addiction, 2 excessively, 3 behaviour,
4 conclusion, 5 certification, 6 suitability,
7 requirements, 8 nutritionists, 9 Findings,
10 unrepresentative, 11 consumption, 12 intake,
13 noticeably, 14 childhood, 15 consequence

LANGUAGE REVIEW 2
1 must have, should have, 2 needn't
have/didn't need to, 3 was able to/managed to,
couldn't/wasn't able to, 4 was raining/had been
raining, left, had stopped, 5 was allowed,
6 must, have to, 7 haven't been
watching/haven't watched, have read, 8 have
known, 9 have won, 10 I was telling you about,
11 which, 12 taking, 13 Nevertheless/Despite
this, 14 to tell, 15 visiting, to buy, 16 going, 17
to become, 18 go, seen, 19 going, driving, 20
was to be held

ENGLISH IN USE
1 of, 2 with, 3 all, 4 whether/if/how, 5 herself,
6 have, 7 being, 8 everything, 9 that/how,
10 so/around/round, 11 would/might, 12 down,
13 When, 14 made, 15 as